HOW TO JUDGE A HOROSCOPE
Volume One

How to Judge a Horoscope

HOW TO JUDGE A HOROSCOPE

Volume One
Volume One

How to Judge a Horoscope

Volume One
I to VI Houses

BANGALORE VENKATA RAMAN

MOTILAL BANARSIDASS PUBLISHERS
PRIVATE LIMITED • DELHI

7th Reprint : Delhi, 2017
Twelfth Edition: Delhi, 1995

ISBN: 978-81-208-0844-7 (Cloth)
ISBN: 978-81-208-0847-8 (Paper)
ISBN: 978-81-208-0846-1 (Cloth Set)
ISBN: 978-81-208-0849-2 (Paper Set)

MOTILAL BANARSIDASS

41 U.A. Bungalow Road, Jawahar Nagar, Delhi 110 007
8 Mahalaxmi Chamber, 22 Bhulabhai Desai Road, Mumbai 400 026
203 Royapettah High Road, Mylapore, Chennai 600 004
236, 9th Main III Block, Jayanagar, Bengaluru 560 011
8 Camac Street, Kolkata 700 017
Ashok Rajpath, Patna 800 004
Chowk, Varanasi 221 001

Printed in India

by RP Jain at NAB Printing Unit,
A-44, Naraina Industrial Area, Phase I, New Delhi–110028
and published by JP Jain for Motilal Banarsidass Publishers (P) Ltd,
41 U.A. Bungalow Road, Jawahar Nagar, Delhi-110007

CONTENTS

PREFACE TO THE ELEVENTH EDITION

To sale of the 10th edition (wrongly printed as 9th edition) of the First Volume of HOW TO JUDGE A HOROSCOPE within twelve months of its publication testify not only to the popularity of my humble writings on astrology but also to the publishing enterprise of Motilal Banarsidass.

I am grateful to the public for the interest they have been evincing in my writings and the patronage extended. I crave the indulgence of the readers for any shortcomings in this edition.

I am thankful to my daughter Gayatri Devi Vasudev for her assistance in revising the edition, to my sons B. Niranjan Babu and B. Sachidananda Babu for careful proof corrections and to Messrs Motilal Banarsidass for printing out this eleventh edition attractively.

Bangalore   **B. V. RAMAN**
3-12-1991

PREFACE TO NINTH EDITION

HOW TO JUDGE A HOROSCOPE is a book on the practical or applied side of astrology. The presentation has been well received by the general public The ninth edition has been thoroughly revised. Volume II dealing with Houses VII to XII has been published.

I am grateful to the public for the interest they have been evincing by my writings and the patronage extended. I crave the indulgence of the readers for any shortcomings in this edition.

I am thankful to my daughter Gayatri Devi Raman for her assistance in thoroughly revising the edition, to my sons B. Niranjan Babu and B. Sachidananda Babu for careful proof corrections and to Messrs. P. N. Kamat and G. K. Ananthram of IBH Prakashana for bringing out this new edition attractively.

BANGALORE
20–4–1984

B. V. RAMAN

PREFACE TO FIRST EDITION

All my astrological books—both predictive and mathematical—have been received favourably—in fact beyond my own expectation—both by the public and the press. This has encouraged me to bring new books dealing with important aspects of astrology. The present work, which I have the pleasure to submit herewith, makes a departure from the conventional method of treatment of astrology. I have dealt with each Bhava or house exhaustively with suitable illustrations. There can therefore be no question as to the importance of this new work.

Nothing is more difficult in the present state of our knowledge than to say in what events and circumstances any given combination will express itself. For example, such a combination as Saturn and the Sun, rising in the ascendant, may result in a fall, disease, loss of status or money; it might indicate a temperamental defect, an intellectual inhibition or it may operate in several other ways. An attempt has been made in the following pages to ascertain the indications of the various influences with reference to each house.

In the judgment of a horoscope an astrologer will come across many a pitfall. Each house deals with different significations and the same set of combinations obtaining in a particular house might influence the different significations comprehended by the house, in different ways. To be more clear, let us take the 4th house. It is supposed to signify mother, education, landed and house properties. An illiterate man may possess many houses and a long-lived mother while one with full education may not possess any properties. How can the same set of combinations affect the same house—in different ways in regard to its different significations? This apparent inconsistency has been reconciled to some extent by the introduction of an important factor, *viz.*, the *Karaka* (indicator). A careful study of the illustrations provided in this book will make these points clear. I have endeavoured in this book to take the reader through the practical aspect of astrology and have omitted the rudimentary principles and rules

In the study of any branch of knowledge, theory and practice must go side by side. Theory always remains theory and it will be of no practical use to man. Take physics, chemistry, biology or geology. One may have read all the books available on the subject but if it comes to a question of application, he blinks like an idiot. An ordinary mechanic, druggist or a compounder is any day more at home with his subject just because he has had practical experience. A harmonious blending of the theoretical knowledge with practical ability is always desirable

In the sphere of astrology too, a study of practical horoscopes is absolutely necessary to grasp the true worth of the subject and handle its technique properly. In writing HOW TO JUDGE A HOROSCOPE, this aim has been kept in view. Typical examples, illustrative of important principles, have been selected from actual lives. A careful study of these examples will certainly give a sound and working knowledge of astrology. In the analysis of the *Bhavas* (houses) I have omitted to take into account the various yogas as I have dealt with them in detail in my *Three Hundred Important Combinations*.

Most of the rules given in ancient Hindu astrological books can be readily tested if we can only secure sufficient data beyond dispute. To reject them off-hand as unsuitable is to betray our ignorance.

In my extensive travels throughout India, I have had discussions with several well-known scientists and scholars. Most of them are convinced that astrology has a rational basis but they hesitate to proclaim their faith in public just because the orthodox scientist has not yet put his stamp of approval on astrology.

In this book, I am not going to make a case for astrology. The introduction I have given to my *Astrology for Beginners* and my *Astrology and Modern Thought* should be eye-openers to the greatest sceptic, that astrology is science and no superstition. It is an interplanetary or cosmic science that deals with the play of cosmic energy. If modern science has not yet discovered by the limited means at its disposal that man is subject to the influences of planets on the three planes of existence, *viz.*, physical, mental and moral, then it is certainly no fault of astrology.

The ancient Maharishis who have propounded the rules of astrology were sages of a high psychic development and examined terrestrial and celestial phenomena by their divine sight or *Divya Drishti*. We would hardly be justified in attributing mean motives to those sages who have left great names in the landmarks of time. They saw many phenomena which the so-called scientist could hardly hope to see with his instruments. Our minds are mean and are almost exclusively engaged in studying and procuring worldly comforts. Though at the height of yogic development, they scorned to utilise such knowledge for any worldly concerns, and soley used it for the benefit of mankind.

Can a science as astrology be ever untrue? The scientist takes too crudely a materialistic view of the whole nature of the universe. He contends that he may think of considering astrology as a fit subject for investigation provided the *destiny* factor is ruled out of it. This is simply absurd. There is nothing like *destiny* in astrology. The proper term to be used is *Adrishta* or that which is not seen. Astrology simply indicates and gives the greatest scope for the development of will-power, by means of which one can either counteract the evil indications or augment the favourable influences.

I feel sure that I have supplied a long-felt want by ushering in this publication for the benefit of the educated public.

BANGALORE
30–9–1941

B. V. RAMAN

1. General Introduction

In the study of astrology nothing is more important, more difficult and more taxing than the proper judgment of a horoscope. The twelve Bhavas or houses represent the entire history of the individual. In order to analyse a horoscope properly and thoroughly each house or Bhava should be carefully scrutinised. Sometimes it so happens that many of the principles of astrology given in even standard works do not hold good in actual charts. In such circumstances, conclusion should not be drawn that the principles of astrology are contradictory. On the other hand, a further analysis of the relations and interrelations of planets should be made.

Astrology is the most difficult of all sciences. It is neither a physical science in the sense that physics or chemistry is; nor is it metaphysical. The precision of mathematics should be harmoniously combined with the intuitive capacity of a philosopher. Consequently no hard and fast rules can be laid down for guidance, except the broad principles. In order to examine a horoscope a good deal of judgment is required.

In this book, it is proposed to deal with the twelve houses in an exhaustive manner and introduce to the reader, principles of astrology with which he may not have come across. One cannot say with any definiteness why particular events of human life are attributed to particular houses in a horoscope. For instance, the first house represents the body while the fourth rules the mother. The rationale of this allocation is still a mystery. The ancient Maharishis must have had in view some scientific basis for the allocation of all the events of human life to the twelve Bhavas or houses.

It must be noted that the twelve houses have reference to the material relation of Jeeva (soul) in its journey from the cradle to the grave. According to one explanation, the ancient Hindu day was divided into twelve sections of five ghatis each and each section was devoted to certain definite duties of the daily routine of living. The day started just about, or a few ghatis (5 ghatis) before sunrise. From this time until sunrise the activities were purely personal. Hence the first house became the personal house. This ingenious explanation does not certainly gratify the curiosity of thinking brains. As the birth gives rise to all the incidents and results to be experienced in our terrestrial life, the ascendant or Lagna, which is their significator, points to the conditions of life on earth. The second half of the day (amongst ancient Hindus) commenced with the seventh period of five ghatis (after the setting in of evening). This period was always a period of amusement and and relaxation—of meeting partners and enjoying the pleasure of contact. Hence the 7th house came to be associated with wife and partner.

The house opposite the ascendant must be one with which to form a pair and therefore the seventh house is attributed to wife. In the zodiac, Aries is the first house. The third house is Gemini. It represents arms. As arms protect our body so also our brothers are our helpers in the earthly life and hence the third house in general indicates brothers. The fourth house rules breasts. It is from the breast that the baby suckles its nourishment while

happiness and pleasure proceed from the mind. It is not
our purpose to try to explain the rationale of the attributes
of the twelve houses. On the other hand we have suggested
above that common-sense thinking enables one to appreciate what this rationale is. Take a haroscope in which the
fifth house is afflicted by unfavourable conjunctions and
aspects. The subject will have no children or all or most
of his children will die. Will this not suffice to prove that
the fifth house is connected with children? The ancient
Maharishis discovered grand and glorious truths with the
aid of *Divya Drishti* or introspection.

In applying the rules contained in astrological books
to practical horoscopes one must definitely bear in mind
that they are merely for his guidance. In addition to
knowledge of astrology, one must also exercise discretion
and common-sense coupled of course with a certain amount
of intuition. Significations have been assigned to the
various dignities and debilities of planets, the *pros* and
cons of which must be carefully considered. No prediction
should be given in a haphazard manner. If the fifth house
is well disposed, and its lord occupies favourable situations
the subject will be happy with regard to children. Supposing Pisces is Lagna and Jupiter is in Cancer the fifth or
suppose Kanya is Lagna and Jupiter is in Makara. Would
the results in either case be the same? In the first instance,
Jupiter lord of Lagna is in the 5th exalted : In the second
case, Jupiter lord of 4th is in debilitation. Can the results
be same in both instances? Common-sense tells us that
the results must differ. An astrological student must bear
in mind all these differences and venture a prediction.

The First house is called *Thanu Bhava*. It deals with
or represents the beginning of life, childhood, health,
environment, personality, the physical body and character.

The *Second house* represents family, face, right eye, food, wealth, literary gift, and manner and source of death, self-acquisition and optimism. The *Third house* rules brothers and sisters, intelligence, cousins and other immediate relations. The *Fourth house* indicates peace of mind, home life, mother, conveyances, house property, landed and ancestral properties, education and neck and shoulders. The *Fifth house* indicates children, grandfather, intelligence, emotions and fame. The *Sixth house* rules over debts, diseases, enemies, miseries, sorrows, illness and disappointments. The *Seventh* represents wife, husband, marriage, urinary organs, marital happiness, sexual diseases, business partner, diplomacy, talent, energies and general happiness. The *Eighth* indicates longevity, legacies and gifts and unearned wealth, cause of death, disgrace, degradation and details pertaining to death. The *Ninth* rules father, righteousness, preceptor, grandchildren, intuition, religion, sympathy, fame, charities, leadership, journeys and communications with spirits. The *Tenth* indicates, occupation, profession, temporal honours, foreign travels, self-respect, knowledge and dignity and means of livelihood. The *Eleventh* represents means of gains ; elder brother and freedom from misery. The *Twelfth* rules losses ; expenditure, waste, extravagance, sympathy, divine knowledge, Moksha and the state after death.

2. Considerations in Judging a House

In examining a house due importance should be given not only to the Rasi but also to the *Navamsa* and other appropriate diagrams. In analysing a Bhava, the following factors should be considered carefully :—

1. The strength, aspects, conjunctions and location of the lord of the house.

2. The strength of the house itself.

3. The natural qualities of the house, of its lord and the planets in it or having aspects.

4. Whether the influence has been altered by any yogas occurring in any particular house or houses.

5. The exaltations and debilitations of the house lords are equally important.

6. The situation—favourable or adverse—of the house-lord or the lord in whose house the particular house-lord is situated, in the Navamsa.

7. The age, position, status and sex of the subject.

8. Each sign has certain planets well disposed or ill-disposed. For instance for those born in Aries the Sun is good. The relation between the house lord (Mars) and the Sun is very important and its proper consideration should not be overlooked.

All these must be properly weighed before any result can be deduced.

If the strength of the lord is full or complete there will be in general a good influence on the house. Among the many events comprehended by a house, those are to be

selected with which the planets are not concerned. The
good or bad nature of the aspects to which a lord or the
house itself is subjected plays no mean part in the judgment of horoscope. The benefic and malefic qualities of
the planets should be taken under all conceivable relations.
The occupations and avasthas of planets go a long way in
directing the results and if well placed good planets are
there, they do good. The *Adhipati* or lord of the house is
responsible to an immense extent for the control of the
house. But if in a particular case, the lord is badly placed,
and the house itself has good conjunctions and aspects
then evil results should not be predicted. When the Dasa
or Bhukti of a house lord comes, the results of the Bhavas
in question will be realised. For instance, lord of Lagna
is weak and is in the 7th house as aspected by malefics.
These combinations indicate more than one wife. During
the Dasa or Bhukti of such a lord, wife's death may be
predicted.

There are hundreds of combinations given for each
house and it is for the reader to try the merits of these
various configurations. These difficulties in the line of
astrological predictions cannot be easily overcome. When
once overcome the student will no doubt be satisfied in
drawing right conclusions.

Astrology is the most difficult and at the same time
the most useful science and one cannot hope to learn the
subject with easy-chair methods. Much effort, concentration and intuition are necessary in order to be a
correct predictor.

Each ascendant has certain planets disposed towards
it favourably, unfavourably and neutrally which I have
enumerated below. My *Hindu Predictive Astrology* may
also be referred to with advantage. The details will be
useful when predicting the results of Dasas.

Benefics and Malefics for each Lagna

If Ascendant or Lagna is : *Aries (Mesha)*.—Jupiter, the Sun and Mars are benefics. Jupiter is the best benefic. The next benefic is Mars. Saturn, Mercury and Venus are malefics. Mercury being the greatest malefic as lord of the 3rd and 6th.

Vrishabha (Taurus).—The best benefic is Saturn as he owns the 9th and 10th. Mercury, Mars and the Sun are also benefics. Jupiter, Venus and the Moon are evil planets but Venus may be declared a neutral as he is lord of Lagna or ascendant.

Mithuna (Gemini).—Venus alone is the most beneficial planet for this Lagna. The most malefic is Mars as he is lord of the 6th and the 11th. Jupiter and the Sun are also evil. The Moon and Mercury may be classified as neutrals.

Kataka (Cancer).—Jupiter and Mars are benefics, the better being Mars as he is lord of the 5th and 10th. Venus and Mercury are evil and Saturn, the Moon and the Sun are neutrals.

Simha (Leo).—Mars and the Sun are benefics, the former being the most auspicious. Mercury and Venus are malefics. Jupiter, the Moon and Saturn are neutrals.

Kanya (Virgo).—Venus is alone the best benefic. Moon, Mars and Jupiter are evil or malefics. Saturn, the Sun and Mercury are neutrals.

Thula (Libra).—Saturn, Mercury and Venus are benefics, Saturn being the best. The Sun, Jupiter and the Moon are malefics. Mars may be taken as a feeble benefic.

Vrischika (Scorpio).—The Moon is the best benefic and Jupiter and the Sun are also benefics. Mercury and Venus are evil. Mars and Saturn are neutrals.

Dhanus (Sagittarius).—Mars and the Sun are benefics. Venus, Saturn and Mercury are evil and Jupiter and the Moon are neutrals.

Makara (Capricorn).—Venus is the most powerful benefic. Mercury and Saturn are also benefics. Mars, Jupiter and the Moon are evil, the worst being Mars. Though the Sun is the 8th lord, he becomes a neutral.

Kumbha (Aquarius).—Venus is the benefic. The Sun and Mars are also benefics. Jupiter and the Moon are malefics and Mercury is a neutral.

Meena (Pisces).—The Moon and Mars are benefics. Saturn, the Sun, Venus and Mercury are malefics. Jupiter is of course a neutral.

To facilitate easy understanding I shall make these principles more clear.

In each horoscope there are benefic lords, malefic lords and neutral lords. These of course have nothing to do with the natural classification of planets as benefics and malefics.

In any horoscope the *benefics* or benefic lords are :— (1) First house lord, other than the Moon ; (2) the 5th and 9th lords (*Thrikonadhipathis*); (3) and (4) lords of the 4th, 7th and 10th when they do not happen to be natural benefics.

The lord of the 9th is decidedly more benefic than the lord of the 5th. Similarly lord of the 10th is more benefic than that of the 7th while the lord of the 4th is the least benefic.

The *malefics* or malefic lords in a horoscope are :— (1) Lords of the 3rd, 6th and 11th houses; (2) lords of the 4th, 7th and 10th houses (*Kendradhipathis*) if they happen to be natural benefics. Again among the malefics the 11th lord is the worst malefic, the 6th less malefic while the 3rd the least malefic.

The *neutrals* in a horoscope are:—(1) The Moon—when he is lord of Lagna, (2) the Sun or the Moon as the 8th lord, (3) the Sun or the Moon as the lords of the 2nd and 12th.

Thus the student has to be very careful in correctly affirming the strengths, weakness and other peculiarities of the horoscope.

From the above it will be seen that a natural benefic, such as for instance Jupiter, can also become a malefic when he is lord of an angle. Natural malefics such as Mars, Saturn, etc., become temproral benefics if they become lords of angles (Kendras). Similarly, natural benefics become malefics if they own quadrangular houses. It is also to be noted that a natural benefic, who becomes a malefic by virtue of quadrangle ownership, will cease to act as a malefic, when he occupies the angular house (Kendra) of which he is lord. Thus in case of Cancer, if Venus occupies Libra, he will cease to be a malefic just because Libra happens to be his own. Similarly, a natural malefic, *viz.*, Mars who becomes a benefic *by virtue of quadrangular ownership* will cease to be a benefic, when he occupies the angular house of which he is the lord.

Yogakarakas

Yogakarakas are planets that confer fame, honour, dignity, financial prosperity, political success, and reputation. Any planet can become yogakaraka when he is a common lord of certain houses. The extent to which he produces a yoga depends upon the strength he has gained by virtue of *Shadbalas* (see my *Graha and Bhava Balas*), association, aspect and occupation.

1. A planet owning both a Kendra (quadrant) and a Trikona (trine) becomes a yogakaraka. This is possible only in case of Mars, Saturn and Venus. In case of

Kataka Lagna (Cancer rising) and *Simha* Lagna (Leo rising)
Mars can officiate as *Yogakaraka* as he becomes lord of
5th and 10th with reference to Cancer and 4th and 9th
from Leo. When the ascendant is *Thula* (Libra) Saturn
owns 4th and 5th—an angle and a trine respectively and
hence he becomes yogakaraka. And when the ascendant
is Taurus, Saturn becomes 9th and 10th lord and hence a
yogakaraka. Venus becomes a yogakaraka, when the
ascendant becomes *Makara* (Capricorn) or *Kumbha*
(Aquarius); in the former case Venus owns the 5th and
10th houses and in the latter case he becomes lord of 4th
and 9th.

2. When a *Kendradhipati* (angular lord) becomes
associated with *Trikonadhipati* (trinal lord), then also, a
Rajayoga is caused. Between these two lords in association, he who is not blemished either by the other ownership (such as 3rd, 6th, etc.) or by associating with lords of
3, 6, 8, becomes the acting yogakaraka. It should be
remembered carefully that the most powerful Rajayoga
could be caused by the association of lords of 9th and
10th. The combination of the lords of the 4th and 5th,
7th and 5th, 10th and 5th, 4th and 9th, 7th and 9th and
10th and 9th is so powerful that it can overcome, to a
large measure, the slight blemish caused by other malefic
lordships.

3. When the 9th and 10th lords have exchanged their
places, each is capable of becoming a *Rajayogakaraka*;
also, when the 9th lord is in the 10th or the 10th lord is in
the 9th, a Rajayoga is caused.

4. When the 9th and 10th lords fully aspect each
other, they will confer Rajayoga.

5. Apart from the Rajayogas referred to above,
certain yogas will be caused due to the position of certain
planets in certain situations. Thus Jupiter and the Moon

mutually aspecting or in mutual quadrants will also confer fame and dignity. There are several Yogas mentioned in Sanskrit works, a detailed list of which will be found in *Satayogamanjari* by B. Suryanarain Rao and in my *Hindu Predictive Astrology*. I have given some typical Yogas in my *Three Hundred Important Combinations*. In all cases, wherever a Rajayoga is noticed, the extent to which it will be realised depends upon the inherent strength it has gained as a result of ownership, association, occupation and aspect of the two planets that cause a Yoga. The Yoga can really be of some substantial effect provided the planets causing the yoga are within 12° of each other. In measuring the yogas or even the general nature of the horoscope, the starting point should be either the ascendant or the Moon, whichever is stronger.

Chart No. 1.—*Born on 12-2-1856 at 12-21 p.m. (L.T.)* *Lat. 18° N., Long. 84° E.*

	Moon Rahu	Lagna	Sat.		Lagna Jupiter	Rahu
Sun Merc. Jupit.						
	RASI				NAVAMSA	
Venus	Mars Ketu			Merc.	Ketu	Sun Saturn Venus Mars	Moon

Balance of Venus Dasa at birth : 12-3-9.

(*a*) The conjunction of the Sun and Mercury (lords of 4th and 5th) in the 10th has resulted in a Rajayoga. This

is not as powerful as the next one because of the blemish
generated by association with Jupiter—lord of 8th and
11th. (b) Saturn is the *Yogakaraka*, as he is lord of 6th
and 10th and occupies the second.

   Chart No. 2.—*Born on 31-7-1897 at 8-10 a.m.
(L.T.) Lat. 12° 20' N., Long. 76° 38' E.*

		Venus		Mercury	Moon Rahu
Rahu	RASI I.61	Sun Ketu	Lagna Moon Merc. Jupiter Mars	NAVAMSA	Sat.
					Lagna
	Saturn			Sun Ketu	Mars Venus	Jupit.

Balance of Ketu Dasa at birth : years 5-0-24.

   (a) The combination of Mars and Jupiter in the
ascendant has produced a Rajayoga. (b) Mars by himself
is a yogakaraka as he is lord of the 4th and 9th.

   The astrologer should possess a keen intellect to enable
him to analyse the various sets of combinations and sift
the evidence properly. For a fuller appreciation of the
modus operandi concerning the interpretation of yogas,
reference may be made to my *Three Hundred Important
Combinations*.

3. Determination of Longevity

Before the period of death is actually determined one should be able to find whether the longevity is long, medium or short, and whether there are *Balarishta* combinations threatening early death. These details have been fully described in standard astrological books to which the reader may conveniently refer. We are at present concerned with the planets who are likely to cause death (Maraka) as a result of certain combinations and associations. For the sake of convenience we may classify the planets who cause death as follows :—

(*a*)   Primary Determinants of death,

(*b*)   Secondary Determinants of death, and

(*c*)   Tertiary Determinants of death.

(*a*)   *Primary Determinants of Death*.—The 3rd and 8th are houses of life and the 2nd and 7th are houses of death.

(i)   Lord of the 2nd or 7th is a determinant of death; (ii)   the (malefic) occupants of these two houses, and (iii)   the (malefic) planets in association with the above lords are also determinants of death.

Of these several determinants above mentioned, planets in conjunction with lords of 2nd and 7th are the most powerful in causing death, while the lords themselves are least powerful.

(*b*)   *Secondary Determinants of Death*.—Above we have referred to the malefic associates with lords of 2nd and 7th and malefic occupants. The following may also become *Marakas* or death-inflicting planets :—

(i) Benefic planets in association with lords of 2nd and 7th, (ii) lordsof 3rd and 8th and (iii) lord of 3rd or 8th associated with 2nd or 7th lord.

(c) *Tertiary Determinants of Death*.—(i) Saturn in conjunction, association or aspect with the Marakas (determinants of death) mentioned above, (ii) lord of the 6th or 8th whether or not he is associated with a *Maraka* planet, and (iii) the least powerful planet in the horoscope.

It is suggested in certain works that the following planets will not cause death. (i) The Sun and the Moon and (ii) the 9th lord. In actual practice, however, this is not found to be true. Herewith is given a list of Marakas in reference to different Lagnas :—

Sign	Maraka
Mesha	— Mercury, Saturn
Vrishabha	— Jupiter, Mars
Mithuna	— Mars, Jupiter
Kataka	— Venus, Mercury
Simha	— Mercury, Venus
Kanya	— Mars, Jupiter
Thula	— Jupiter
Vrischika	— Mercury, Venus, Saturn
Dhanus	— Venus, Saturn
Makara	— Mars, Jupiter
Kumbha	— Mars
Meena	— Mercury, Saturn, Venus

Instances are wanting to prove that the above assignment of so-called Marakas always holds good.

Because the ascendant is *Dhanus*, Marakas are Venus and Saturn. At birth Mars ruled for years 4–7–27. The native died in Saturn's Dasa Saturn's Bhukti. Saturn is

Chart No. 3.—*Born on 28–7–1897 at 6–47 p.m. (L.T.)*
Lat. 12° 20' N., Long. 76° 38' E.

	Venus	Moon	Sun Merc.		Mars	Rahu	
			Ketu	Sun			Sat.
Rahu	RASI		Mars Jupit.	NAVAMSA			Jupit.
Lagna	Saturn			Venus	Ketu	Lagna Mercury	Moon

Balance of Mars Dasa at birth : years 4-7-27.

lord of 2nd and 3rd and is in the 12th from Lagna and 7th
from the radical Moon.

Chart No. 4—*Born on 11–4–1880 at 10-38 a.m. L.T.*
Lat. 18° 5' N., Long. 83° 28' E.

Sun Saturn Jupiter Venus Merc.	Moon		Lagna Ketu Mars	Sun Sat. Ketu	Lagna		
	RASI				NAVAMSA		Venus
	III.58						Moon Rahu Merc. Jupit.
Rahu				Mars			

Balance of Venus Dasa at birth : Years 13–3–20

Because in Chart No. 4 Mithuna is Lagna, Marakas are Jupiter and Mars. (*a*) Jupiter as lord of the 7th becomes a primary determinant of death. (*b*) Rahu is a Maraka as he is in the 7th house. (*c*) Mercury is with lord of the 7th and owns the 3rd and 6th from the Moon. The native died on 1-7-1941 when the sub-period of Mercury was operating in the major period of Jupiter.

Chart No. 5 is an elusive horoscope. The lord of Lagna is exalted in the 5th without any unfavourable aspects, conjunctions or associations. This has conferred Purnayu or full term of life. Planets supposed to be Marakas did not kill the subject; the foundation of the horoscope is strong. The native died on 7-8-1940 at about 12 noon in Guru Dasa, Guru Bhukti. In the Navamsa, Guru gets Maraka power and the Lagna aspected by Mars.

Chart No. 5—*Born on 7/6-5-1861 at 4-5 a.m. (L.T.) Lat. 22° 40' N. Long. 88° 30' E.*

Lagna Moon	Venus Sun Mercury	Mars	Ketu		Jupit. Lagna			Ketu
			Jupit.		Moon			
	RASI					NAVAMSA		Merc. Sat.
Rahu			Sat.			Sun Rahu Venus		Mars

Balance of Mercury Dasa at birth: Years 10–2–12.

The student should collect a number of horoscopes of persons dead and apply the principles given in this chapter. Chart No. 5 is complicated and defies the intelligence of the average astrologer.

Of course in the determination of death, the transiting influences have a great bearing. Saturn was transiting the 2nd from the radical Moon when the native of this chart died.

In Chart No. 6 the Ascendant is Gemini and the Marakas are Mars and Jupiter. But Saturn (lord of 8) killed the native at the close of his Dasa. Saturn is in the 6th from Lagna and 7th from the Moon.

Chart No. 6—*Born on 18–3–1869 at 1–15 p.m. (G.M.T.) Lat. 51° N., Long. 0° 5' W.*

Sun Jupit.		Moon	Lagna	Mars Jupit.	Venus	
Venus Merc.	RASI		Mars Rahu	Sat. Moon	NAVAMSA	Ketu
Ketu	11.72			Rahu		Sun
	Saturn			Merc.	Lagna	

Balance of Sun Dasa at birth: Years 2–1–25.

Ascendant is *Vrischika* or Scorpio. Marakas are Mercury, Venus and Saturn. Death occurred in the subperiod of Rahu in Saturn's Dasa. Saturn is lord of 3rd and occupies the 8th, aspected by Mercury, 8th and 11th lord.

2

Chart No. 7.—*Born on 2-12-1885 at 6-13 a.m. (L.T.) Lat. 9° 43' N., Long. 76° 13' E.*

Ketu		Sat.		Lagna	Jupiter		Merc.
					Venus Sat.		Ketu
	RASI					NAVAMSA	
Venus	II.118	Mars		Rahu			Moon
Merc.	Lagna Sun	Moon Rahu Jupit.		Sun			Mars

Balance of Mars Dasa at birth : Years 6–0–24.

Careful observation reveals that many apparently healthy children, with every circumstance in their favour, succumb to early death, while many puny and sickly children have been reared by careful nursing and judicious treatment. I have with me horoscopes of several weak and sickly children who according to the best medical diagnosis should have died early but who, according to astrology, were destined to live. For testing the rules of astrology we should have sufficient *data* bayond dispute. A child was born in Dublin on 20–11–1887 at 3–40 p.m. The child lived for 20 hours. The Lagna is Taurus with the Moon in it aspected by the Sun in Scorpio. Another male child born on 6–8–1912 at 42.5 ghatis after sunrise (5 h. 10m. 20s E. Long. and 13° N. Lat.) died in the 14th month. The ascendant (Aries) is hemmed inbetween Rahu and Saturn. The Moon is afflicted by conjunction with Saturn. A female infant was born at 3h. 20m. p.m. on 1–2–1874 near Dublin. The ascendant was Cancer with the Moon there. The Sun and Saturn were in Capricorn aspecting this combination. The child died on 19–2–1874 of marasmus (congenital). Generally if the Lagna, the Sun and the Moon are afflicted, the child dies early.

The Maraka question, that is the determination of the source, nature, time and place of death, has been elaborately discussed in the second part of this book to be published in due course.

4. Concerning the First House

In the delineation of any house, it is the Bhava that is
important and not the Rasi.   The difference between the
Rasi and Bhava is explained in my books on Mathematical
Astrology*.   The Navamsa is also equally important. The
effects of the Navamsa during which a person happens to
be born are supposed to influence all his activities throughout life, subject to modifications according to the aspects
of planets situated at different places with reference to the
Navamsa.   It is the pivot on which the horoscope revolves.
Consequently Hindu Astrology attaches the greatest importance to the Navamsa chart. Every combination mentioned
should be applied to the Rasi, Bhava and Navamsa charts
and then a conclusion drawn.   Essentials of judgement
have been described in my other works and it would be
sheer waste of space if they were repeated here.

Judgment is the summing up of the influence of planets
in a horoscope.   Several elements are required for judging
a horoscope, *viz.*, (*a*) the house, (*b*) its lord, (*c*) its occupants, and (*d*) its Karaka or indicator.   It must be noted
that the functions of a lord are those of the house or
houses owned by him.   Apart from this, each lord has his
own *Karaka* or inherent functions.   For example, if we
take the 7th house in a horoscope in which Aquarius is
ascendant, the functions of the lord of the house, *viz.*, the
Sun are two-fold : the function house, due to ownership

* *a*) *A Manual of Hindu Astrology* (*b*) *Graha and Bhava Balas.*

and the *Karaka* function, *viz.*, governance over father. Judgment should therefore be based upon the (*a*) position of the house lord, (*b*) aspects and association of the house lord, (*c*) the yogas, etc., formed by the house lord and other modifications. This holds good in the Navamsa also.

The celebrated Satyacharya opines that one's complexion, caste, physical appearance, mental characteristics, nature of birth, fame and defame, success, etc., should all be based on the strength or otherwise of the Lagna and the Karaka.

Results of Lord of First House Occupying Different Houses

In the *First House:* The subject lives by his own exertion, will have an independent spirit and will have two wives or one married and another illegal.

If the Lagnadhipati is well disposed in Lagna, the person becomes famous in his own community and country.

The reader must note that the combination is of general application. The exact nature of the results should be interpreted by taking into account the strength, weakness and other factors attendant upon the house lord. If *Lagnadhipati* is in Lagna and aspected by evil planets, the results produced will be quite different from those which he would have produced by being aspected by benefics. The same rules apply to all Bhavas which should be borne in mind by every reader.

Second House : There will be more of gains, teased or worried by enemies, good character respectable and generous hearted.

Well disposed. He will gladly discharge his duties towards his kith and kin, and will be ambitious. He will possess prominent eyes and be blessed with forethought.

Third House : Makes one highly couragious, fortunate, reepectable, two wives, intelligent and happy.

When Lagnadhipati is well disposed, the native's rise in life will be brought about by his brothers. He may become famous as a musician or a mathematician depending upon the nature of the sign and the planets involved.

Fourth House : There will be happiness from parents, many brothers, materialistic, well built, fair looking and well-behaved.

If the 4th lord is favourably disposed, the person will acquire considerable landed properties, specially through maternal sources. He will be rich, happy, famous and commands a number of conveyances.

Fifth House : The first child does not survive, not much happiness from children, short tempered, subservient and serving others.

If fortified : In the good graces of rulers or powerful political parties and likely to be absorbed into trade or diplomatic services. He will propitiate deities consistent with the indications of the fifth lord.

Sixth House : In addition to the results produced by the lord of Lagna being in the third, the following may also be noted. There will be bebts but they will be liquidated when the Dasa of the Lagndhipati comes.

When the lord is fortified, the native joins the army, becomes a Commander or even a Commander-in-chief provided the lord's Dasa operates at the opportune period. Or, he may become head of medical or health services or an expert physician or surgeon. Here the *other influences* should be suitably balanced.

Seventh House : The wife does not live or there will be more than one marriage. Later in life becomes detached from worldly affairs and tries to lead an ascetic life.

Depending upon other factors the subject will either be rich or poor. There will be much travelling.

If well disposed, he will spend most of his time in foriegn countries and lead a licentious life. Or he will be a puppet in the hands of his parents-in-law.

Eighth House: Learned, gambling tendencies, interested in occultism and mean character.

If the lord is strong the native takes pride in helping others, has a number of friends, religiously inclined and will have a peaceful and sudden end.

Ninth House: Generally fortunate, protector of others, religious; if a Hindu—worshipper of Vishnu, good orator, happiness on account of wife and children; and rich.

Provided the lord is well disposed, he will inherit good ancestral and paternal property. The father will be famous, philanthropic and god-fearing.

Tenth House: In addition to the results of the 4th house, there will be professional success, honoured by eminent men, a research scholar or specialisation in that branch of knowledge or profession which is represented by lord of Lagna and the 10th.

Eleventh House: In addition to the results of the 2nd house, there will always be gains in business if a businessman. The subject will not experience financial straits.

He owes his prosperity to his elder brother. He will earn enormous business profits, consistent with the indications of the other planets joining the combination.

Twelfth House: The same results as in the 8th are produced. In addition, there will be many losses, visiting holy places and no success in business enterprises.

He will spend inherited riches on charities and other deserving causes. Emotionally balanced he will dedicate himself for public weal.

Other Important Combinations

If the lord of birth in birth with lord of 6th, 8th or 12th, conjunction with or aspected by malefics, the health will suffer. If there are any beneficial aspects this evil should not be predicted. If the ascendant lord is posited in the Lagna subject to evil combinations, the native will not be physically happy. If all the planets aspect the ascendant he will be strong, wealthy and long-lived. If the lord is strong and good planets are in kendras and the ascendant is not aspected by evil planets, there will be great happiness regarding body. If the lord of birth is in conjunction with an evil planet and Rahu occupies Lagna, the person has fears from deception. If Rahu, Mars and Saturn occupy the ascendant, the person will have some trouble in his sexual organs.

If Jupiter or Venus remains in quadrants or trines from Lagna, favourable results are produced. If the lord of the Lagna is in a movable sign aspected by its own lord his health will always be good and fortune prosperous. If the ascendant lord is in the 8th, the subject will have a weak constitution. Provided favourable aspects exist, this result should not be predicted. *The native* will have a sickly constitution if the lord of the house in which Lagnadhipati is situated is also disposed unfavourably. If Saturn is in the ascendant, his things will be stolen or he will be cheated. He will be wounded in the head if lord of Lagna be Mars or Saturn and the house is occupied or aspected by evil planets. If a *Sushka* (dry) planet occupies the Lagna the person will be lean. (*Sushka* planets are the Sun, Mars and Saturn). If the ascendant falls in any of the *Sushka* Rasis (signs owned by Mars, Saturn and the Sun) the body will be emanciated. If the lord of the Lagna is in conjunction with *Sushka* planets then also similar results will follow. He will be corpulent if ascendant be Cancer, Scorpio, or Pisces with good planets. If the ascendant lord is a watery planet (Venus and the Moon), strong and well conjoined, the native becomes stout. Corpulence can also be predicted if the Lagna is owned by a benefic and if the lord of the Navamsa occupied by the lord of Lagna occupies a watery sign. If Jupiter occupies Lagna or if Jupiter aspects Lagna from a watery sign or if the Lagna happens to be a watery sign with benefics in it then also the body will be stout.

The subject will suffer from asthma or lung troubles, if the Sun is in the ascendant aspected by Mars. Suffers from wounds and accidents if Mars is in Lagna aspected by the Sun or Saturn. If the ascendant, its lord, ascendant in Navamsa, or its lord is in a movable sign the subject travels in distant lands with profit to himself. He will be happy all his life if lord of Lagna is in *Vargottama*, in exaltation, in a friendly drekkana, and joined or aspected by good planets. If benefics stay in the 1st, 11th and 12th houses and the strong lord is in Trikonas he will be happy in the beginning and middle. If lord of Lagna is strong or Jupiter is in Lagna he will be happy in the beginning.

Given above are combinations which enable one to analyse in a general manner the first house and attempt predictions regarding the physical appearance, general fortune, health, stature, etc., of the native. Real advancement can easily be made if the principles enumerated in these articles are applied to actual charts. If the Lagna or its lord is hemmed in between two malefics, preferably Saturn and Rahu, the native will encounter thieves and suffer on their account. Rahu in the 12th is not as harmful as in the 2nd while Saturn in the 2nd is not as harmful as in the 12th.

If there are many evil planets in Lagna the person will always be miserable. If the ascendant lord, or the lord of the Navamsa occupied by the lord of the Lagna, or the lord of the 11th occupy the second house the person becomes happy after his 20th year. The position of the above lords in kendras makes the person happy after the 30th year. Occupation of the 9th house by Lagna lord is conducive for happiness after the 16th year.

Lord of Lagna in a decent position is itself a great asset which sustains a person throughout his life. Added to this the presence of any planet or planets in the 10th adds greater vigour. Added to these two, that horoscope is a fortunate one in which planets are not disposed in *Dwirdwadasa* positions (12th and 2nd from each other).

A careful study of a large number of horoscopes has revealed that when Lagnadhipati is not strong and well disposed, but occupies the 3rd (vipat), 5th (pratyak) and 7th (naidhana) constellations from Janma Nakshatra (the star held by the radical Moon), the evil indications would be intensified. Conversely when Lagnadhipati is strong but occupies the above constellational positions, there will be a lessening of the favourable indications. Even when Lagnadhipati is strong but the lord of sign occupied by Lagnadhipati is blemished, the benefic results decrease and the malefic effects are augmented. In analysing Lagna Bhava, due attention must be paid to the dispositions of Chandra Lagna and Navamsa Lagna also.

We shall examine some actual horoscopes and then continue further the discussion of the first house.

The lord of Lagna in Chart No. 8 is Venus who is a benefic. The ascendant is aspected by a malefic Mars. Though an enemy of Venus, Jupiter is a benefic. Consequently the location of Lagnadhipati in the house of

Chart No. 8.—*Born on 12–2–1856 at 12–21 p.m. (L.T.) Lat. 18° 18′ N., Long. 83° 58′ E.*

	Moon Rahu	Ascdt.	Sat.		Ascdt. Jupiter	Rahu	
Sun Merc. Jupit.		RASI			NAVAMSA		
Venus		Mars Ketu		Merc.	Ketu	Sun Saturn Venus Mars	Moon

Balance of Venus Dasa at birth: Years 12–3–9.

Jupiter is auspicious. The presence of Lagnadhipati in the 8th made the native a very learned man. Coming to the Navamsa, lord of Lagna aspects Lagna and hence, good. Jupiter, lord of the 9th, occupies Lagna. Venus situated in his own house aspects Lagna. Saturn exalted and the Sun debilitated aspect Lagna. Hence the first house has acquired considerable strength. Since lord of Navamsa Lagna is in a movable sign, and the Lagna itself is a movable sign, the subject had wide travels. The stature was ordinary. The subject was fair looking. (Mark Venus and Mars, lords of Lagna and the Navamsa Lagna are fair planets.) The height was of medium size, complexion good. On account of the aspect of Mars, he was martial in nature. There are other combinations which need not be mentioned here which made the native one of the world's greatest personalities. The position of the three planets in the 10th and the formation of *Rajayogas* are factors whose bearing on the greatness of the native can never be overlooked.

Chart No. 9.—*Born on 22-2-1863 at 10-16 p.m. (L.T.) Lat. 13° N., Long. 5h. 10m. 20s. E.*

	Moon	Mars Ketu		Ascdt.		Saturn	Venus
Venus Sun —— Merc.							Moon Ketu Merc.
	RASI			Sun Mars Rahu	NAVAMSA		
	Rahu	Jupit. Ascdt.	Sat.	Jupit.			

Balance of Ketu Dasa at birth :   Years 0-9-29.

It will be seen at once that, both in the Rasi and in the Navamsa, planets are in the 2nd and 12th from each other and hence unfavourable. Lagna is Libra and its lord Venus is in the 5th with the Sun who is a malefic and who is also the lord of the 11th from Lagna. Lagna is aspected by the Moon. It is hemmed in between Rahu and Saturn in the 2nd and 12th respectively. The subject, though belonging to a respectable family, was an ordinary man. Though Lagna is a movable sign, its lord is in a fixed sign. The subject had absolutely no travels.

In Chart No. 8, the ascendant lord is Venus and he is in the 8th from the ascendant. On either side of the ascendant are Rahu (in the 12th with the Moon) and Saturn (in the 2nd). Here the opposite holds good. That is, Rahu is in the 2nd without any favourable aspects

whatsoever and Saturn is in the 12th.   On account of this
combination the subject suffered from the hands of thieves
and robbers and sustained some injuries.

Chart No. 10.—*Born on 8-8-1912 A.D. at 7-35 p.m.
(I.S.T.) Lat, 13° N., Long. 5h. 10m. 20s. E.*

Rahu	Moon Saturn		Saturn	Venus
Asdt.		Sun	Sun Rahu	
	RASI II.72	Mars Merc. Venus	Ascdt.	NAVAMSA	Ketu Moon Merc.
	Jupiter	Ketu	Jupiter	Mars

Balance of Mars Dasa at birth: Years 6-1-6.

Lord of Lagna Saturn is in Taurus, a friendly sign
and in conjunction with the Moon lord of the 6th.   Lord
of Lagna is also aspected by Jupiter and Lagna itself is
aspected by Mars, Mercury and Venus.   Again in the
Navamsa, Saturn lord of Lagna is in debilitation and
Lagna is aspected by Mars.   As Saturn has more to do
with first house than any other planet, the person's physical
features are predominantly saturnine.   He is tall, lean,
with much hair, fair on account of the aspects of Mars
over Lagna and Jupiter over Lagnadhipati.   Since the first
house planet is a malefic and since he is in conjunction
with the Moon, the native will not be quite healthy.   The
exact nature of his ill-health should be ascertained from
the 6th house.

It will be seen that an examination of a number of horoscopes will make it clear that the ascendant lord in situations similar to the above illustration will confer a weak constitution. A planet may give a weak constitution but at the same time it may also produce financial and professional prosperity.

Results of Different Signs Ascending

Each sign of the zodiac when ascending imprints its own definite characteristics, mental, physical and personal. These have of course to be blended with those of planets rising or aspecting. The following delineations are for signs alone without any planet in the first house. If any planet be there, it will modify these testimonies. *The Sun* adds nobleness to the figure and increases health of the constitution. *The Moon* indicates better proportion and greater delicacy of figure. *Mars* gives a fair ruddiness to the person, healthy constitution, sturdy figure, a temperament principally of heat and dryness. *Mercury* makes the stature proportionately well shaped, bodily temperament chiefly hot and yellowish complexion. *Jupiter* gives a fair complexion, large eyes and dignified stature. *Venus* produces qualities of a nature more applicable to feminity, beauty, softness and greater delicacy of form. *Saturn,* black and curled hair, tall figure, inactive and narrow chest.

The mental disposition should always be judged by reference to the Moon and his disposition. The dispositions given below are of a general nature. In actual practice, however, they will be seen to vary from the normal in some respects, owing to the strength of the ruling sign, its ruler, planets aspecting the ascendant, etc.

The liability to diseases and accidents is judged from

the planets rising or setting, and those configured with
the Moon. When the Sun, the Moon and the ascendant
are afflicted by more than one of the malefics, liability to
accidents and a violent or sudden death is indicated.
Should Rahu and Ketu be in angles with the Sun and the
Moon, the angles being Aries, Taurus, Scorpio and Capricorn, the body will be afflicted with distortions, lameness,
or even paralysis.

Mesha (Aries) Rising

Mental Tendencies.—Independent thinking, courageous
and sensitive.

Physical Tendencies.—Middle stature, ruddy complexion, sharp sight, long face and neck, head broad at
the temples and narrow at chin, brown or light and curly,
mark or scar on the head or temples, teeth well-set and
round eyes.

General Tendencies.—Those born in Mesha are lovers
of scientific thought. They are enterprising and ambitious.
They have the ability to plan. They dislike being guided
by others ; are intense when interested, vehement when
excited. They are rather stubborn, but often frank.
Quick tempered, they resent imposition and are liable to
go to extremes. Their constitution will be hot. They love
beauty, art and elegance. They have practical ideas. If
Aries is afflicted they suffer from diseases pertaining to the
head. Mental affliction and derangement are also likely
if Saturn and the Moon are in Aries.

Vrishabha (Taurus) Rising

Mental Tendencies.—Obstinate, proud and ambitious, easily accessible to adulation but affectionate and
loving, sometimes unreasonable, prejudiced and stubborn.

Physical Tendencies.—The stature of the person born in this sign will be short and often tending towards corpulence, lips thick and complexion swarthy, square build of the body. Face beautiful, eyes and ears large, full forehead, hands plump and broad.

General Tendencies.—If they are not listened to attentively, people born in this sign will act like a bull. They are self-reliant. They have their own principles and ways and a piercing intellect. They have a great deal of endurance, latent power and energy. They always put their ideas into practice. Their physical powers and mental endurance are indeed noteworthy. They are fond of pleasure, they love beauty and music. They possess a magnetic personality. They think they are born for exercising authority. They generally suffer from nervous complaints after the fiftieth year. With regard to children much happiness is not indicated. The late Prof. B. Suryanarain Rao was a typical example of Taurus ascending.

Mithuna (Gemini) Rising

Mental Tendencies.– They will have a wavering mind. Fond of writing and reading they are ingenious and quick-witted, vivacious and inconsistent, nervous and restless.

Physical Tendencies.—They are tall and straight in stature and active in motion. Face well developed, there is a depression near the chin, a thin face, sanguine complexion, unusual height if malefics are there, the eyes are clear and the nose snub. They are weak but active.

General Tendencies.—They are very active and tend to become experts in mechanical sciences. They may suffer sudden nervous breakdowns. They must be cautious in moving with the opposite sex. Their mind will be often conscious of their own depravity. They are very clever and possess inherent conversational and literary ability. They are liable to fraud and deception. If evil planets are in Gemini, trickery and deceit will characterise their nature. They are best in occupations where there is much activity.

Kataka (Cancer) Rising

Mental Tendencies.—People born in this sign will be extremely sensitive, inquisitive, nervous and restless, interested in music and dexterous.

Physical Tendencies.—They have a middle sized body, face full, slightly snub nose, fair complexion, long arms, long face and wide chest.

General Tendencies.—They are very intelligent, bright and extremely frugal and equally industrious. Their frugality often takes the form of miserliness. The mind is intuitional, perceptive. They like pleasure. They are deeply attached to their family and children. They often meet with disappointment in love affairs. They are very talkative, self-reliant, honest and unbending. They will have a reputation for love of justice and fairplay. Their emotions are strong. They have psychic tendencies, are receptive to new ideas and adapt themselves to environment. They are desirous of possessions and cautious. They can best take up occupations of a fluctuating nature.

Simha (Leo) Rising

Mental Tendencies.—People born in Leo are ambitious as well as avaricious, warm-hearted, and have a liking for art, literature and music. They are cheerful and unimpulsive.

Physical Tendencies.—Persons born in this sign will be magnetic in appearance with broad shoulders, bilious

3

constitution, of average height, oval faced, thoughtful countenance and the upper part of the body is generally better formed.

General Tendencies.—They can adapt themselves to any condition in life. They have faith. In affection they are sincere. They stick to orthodox principles in religion but are perfectly tolerant. Generally good tempered, they are sensitive. They are lovers of music, literature and possess a certain amount of philosophical knowledge. They are voracious readers. In life they do not succeed as much as they would like to and often throughout they struggle very much. Their ambitions remain unfulfilled to a great extent. They lack a natural policy and hence get into many difficulties. They are forgiving and do not hold a grudge long. They are likely to suffer from nervous troubles and are generally misunderstood by their superiors and bosses.

Kanya or Virgo Rising

Mental Tendencies.—Those born in Virgo are impulsive, emotional and fond of learning. They love music and fine arts. They lack self-confidence. Methodical and ingenious, they have active minds.

Physical Tendencies.—Persons born in this sign will be middle-sized. Their chest will be prominent and when afflicted, weak also. They have a straight nose, cheeks massive and the forehead, good.

General Tendencies.—They exhibit their intelligence when quite young. They are discriminating and emotional and get easily carried away by impulse. They are cautious regarding their own interests, prudent, economical, diplomatic and shrewd. As authors they make progress in physical and chemical sciences. They acquire much power and influence over others. They are liable to suffer from nervous breakdowns and paralysis when the sign is afflicted. They are of a speculative nature.

Thula (Libra) Rising

Mental Tendencies.—Persons born in Libra are idealistic, quick-witted, vindictive, forceful and positive.

Physical Tendencies.—They generally possess fair complexion, a middle-sized stature, phlegmatic constitution, handsome appearance, broad face, fine eyes, broad chest and regular features. Their appearance will be generally youthful.

General Tendencies.—People born in this sign are generally of a sensual disposition. They are keen observers of human nature. They have keen foresight and reason out things from the standpoint of their own views. They love justice, peace, order and are agreeable persons. They are ambitious. They are more idealists than realists or practical men and often contemplate on schemes that are like building castles in the air. They are not sensitive to what others say of them. As political leaders and religious reformers they exert tremendous influence over the masses and sometimes their zeal and enthusiasm can go to such a pitch that they can force their views upon unwilling minds. They are not easily amenable to reason. They are great lovers of music. Truth and honesty have a special appeal for them.

Vrischika (Scorpio) Rising

Mental Tendencies.—Sarcastic and impulsive, a female born in this sign will be masculine in nature. Interested in occult forms of study they possess a subtle mind, hard to influence.

Physical Tendencies.—Persons born in this sign are handsome in appearance. The bones are well developed.

They have broad eyes, tall figure, curly hair and broad forehead. The personality is forceful with prominent brows and preceptive faculties.

General Tendencies.—They will have a generous disposition. They are exceedingly fickle-minded and love much excitement. Though inclined to sensual things in reality, they will not hesitate to philosophise upon the virtues of controlling sensual pleasures. They are good correspondents. They are often brutal, brusque and keenly fond of contest. They possess enterprise. They appreciate luxury but are frugal. They may become expert musicians if they learn that art. They can also become proficient in fine arts, dancing and the like. They uphold their own views. Their constitution will be hot and they are liable to suffer from piles. They are good conversationalists as well as writers and often rely too much on their own intelligence.

Dhanus (Sagittarius) Rising

Mental Tendencies.—Those born in Sagittarius have an inclination for philosophy and occult studies. They can acquire great mastery in these subjects. Humane and somewhat impulsive, they are generally active and enterprising.

Physical Tendencies.—Persons born in this sign are generally inclined towards corpulence. They possess almond eyes and their hair is brown. They are usually good looking. Evenly set teeth, a happy smile, and fullness of the figure characterise the natives of Dhanus.

General Tendencies.—They are of a phlegmatic temperament. They are too conventional and also business-like. They are prompt and uphold conservative views. They are sympathetic and loving, and possess good foresight. At times they are restless and over-anxious. They are too callous and enthusiastic. They hate all external show. They are God-fearing, honest, humble and free from hypocrisy. They exercise strict control over their food and drinks and in regard to their relations with the opposite sex. They are prone to be misunderstood unintentionally by others. In late years they must be careful about their lungs as they are liable to suffer from rheumatic pains and the like.

Makara (Capricorn) Rising

Mental Tendencies.—They are stoical to the miseries of life. Possessed of sympathy, generosity and philanthropy, self-willed, strong in purpose, secretive and vindictive, Capricorn natives are cunning and determined.

Physical Tendencies.—Persons born in this sign are tall, lean, reddish-brown in colour with prominent stiff hair on the eye-brows and the chest. The head is big and the face fairly broad. They have large teeth, a big mouth, prominent nose, and are inclined to stoop. The body is thin and fleshy.

General Tendencies.—They have a knack to adapt themselves to circumstances. They have great aspirations in life and cannot economise funds. They like a lot of show. Noted for their perseverance. They become vindictive when Saturn is afflicted and may become somewhat bigoted. They are capable of much endeavour. In the home life they are perfectionists and often cannot get on well with husbands or wives. They should check this harmful tendency on their part. They are industrious. If Mars occupies any sign other than his own they lack confidence, become funky, nervous and weak-minded. They can be described as "chatter-boxes" and have little or no control over their tongues.

Kumbha (Aquarius) Rising

Mental Tendencies.—Aquarius being a philosophica sign, people born in it become great teachers, writers, and lecturers, provided the sign is free from afflictions. Natives of Aquarius are reserved, they are peevish when provoked, generous hearted, highly sympathetic and are always bent upon helping others. They are intelligent, good memory and capable of dealing with facts.

Physical Tendencies.—They are generally tall and lean with countenance, handsome, appearance attractive and disposition elegant. Their lips are flushy, cheeks are broad and they have prominent temples and buttocks. If Saturn is in the 4th, the chest will be weak with a tendency towards stooping.

General Tendencies.—They make friends of others very soon. They are peevish and when provoked, rise like a bulldog but their anger is easily subsided. They shine very well as authors and writers. Their conversation is always interesting. They are sometimes timid and funky. They feel shy to exhibit their talents before new audiences. They specialise in subjects like astrology and become great upholders of some such cause. Their literary greatness comes before the world when they are quite young. Unless the planetary positions are otherwise favourably situated, people born in this sign will suffer certain critical setbacks which will jeopardise their reputation. Owing to their humanitarian doctrines they are prone to be misunderstood. In family life, they will not have sufficient happiness. They will be much devoted to their husbands or wives. They are liable to suffer from colic troubles, chest pain and the like. They should always be kept happy in life by their husbands or wives. Otherwise their health will suffer.

Meena (Pisces) Rising

Mental Tendencies.—Persons born in Pisces are stubborn, psychically receptive, highly religious, stoical, bigotted and God-fearing.

Physical Tendencies.—They are fair, stout of middle-sized height, swarthy in complexion, eyes, 'piscean', and inclined towards corpulence.

General Tendencies.—They are respectors of orthodoxical principles and can forego anything but orthodoxy. They are extremely superstitious. They are very reserved and are liable to draw premature conclusions on any matter. They are God-fearing and very rigid in the observance of religious customs and practices. They are stubborn, rather timid, and ambitious to exercise authority over others. They rarely realise their ambitions. They are restless and fond of history, antiquarian talks and mythological masterpieces. They are frugal in spending money and though generally dependent upon others throughout their life, still bear a mark of independence. They are just in their dealings and fear to transgress the laws of truth. With all this they lack self-confidence.

Planets in the First House

Planets rising in the ascendant produce their own influences. *Prima facie* it seems absurd that the accidental positions of planetary bodies at the moment of birth of a child influence his health, finance, fortunes, affections and disposition throughout his earthly career. But experiment has shown that there is an intimate connection between the positions of planets at the time of birth and a baby's material and moral dispositions. The horoscope should be considered as a person and not as a set of disconnected planetary influences. There is something that links up these scattered and contradictory fragments into a connected and coherent whole. The twelve houses represent not only the mould in which the young life takes shape at birth, but they are unalterable as to their primary significance when affected by the planets at birth. Diagnosis of any chart may be obtained when we first show the effects of the different planets being situated in the different signs.

The interpretations given below are for the planets by their positions in the houses only, unaspected. If a planet situated in the first house is aspected by or is in conjunction with any other planet, then its effects by house position, as given below are subjected to modification correspondingly. The details given below must be adopted to suit the requirements of the horoscope in question. First see whether in the first house, any planet is exalted or debilitated and whether the planet in the first house has caused any special yogas, etc. (This principle applies to all other houses also.) Then modify the reading accordingly. For example, Aquarius is the ascendant and Saturn is rising there. The disposition is calm, serious and grave. The native is faithful. Since Aquarius is the ascendant the good qualities of Saturn will further manifest as lord of the rising sign is in his own house. If Leo is the rising sign then the horoscope becomes generally unfortunate, indicates many sorrows, disappointments, poverty and an uphill road generally. By using considerable discretion-qualifying or moderating your deductions to conform with the astrological testimonies—you can unfold your powers of prediction. Summing up, the above remarks:—
(a) consider the nature of the rising planet, (b) whether it is in debility or exaltation, in a friendly or inimical sign, (c) note the aspects it receives from the planets—the houses from which aspects are cast and the conjunctions the rising planet has, (d) the nature of the sign—movable,

immovable, common, airy, watery etc. Finally, blend all the influences carefully.

Sun in the First House.—Strong moral nature, righteous-minded, ambition and love of power, tends to be well supported by good health and vitality. Cheerfulness and an optimistic temperament help to ensure popularity. It adds respect to the personality and gives lofty motives. If with Saturn or Mars, it indicates scars and a hot constitution. The blood becomes impure and there will be itches all over the body. Fevers, inflammations and eye affections may also be anticipated.

Moon in the First House.—The native becomes fanciful and romantic, a moderate eater. Considerable restlessness is usually tempered by an easy-going disposition. The fortune is generally changing. It makes one an idealist, a great traveller and explorer. If with Saturn, the mind will always be worried. If Mars is with the Moon, it indicates menstrual disorders in the case of women. Sociability tends to be a strong feature. He will be successful in professions that bring him into contact with the masses. The Moon in Lagna with Rahu indicates hysterical tendencies and with Jupiter, the mind is elevated.

Mars in the First House.—This gives a hot constitution, courage, self-confidence and enterprise. The native will possess practical ability and love of liberty and independence. He becomes reckless of danger scorning defeat. This gives somewhat of a rash nature. The body will have scars and the appearance will be handsome. The domestic life will be unhappy unless there are other favourable combinations. Abuse of physical resources may lead to ill-health. There is a proneness to accidents. The aspects should be carefully examined. Danger of cuts, burns, etc., are likely.

Mercury in the First House.—This position makes the subject humorous. Quickness of wit and mental ingenuity tend to be strongly marked. The native becomes well-read, particularly in occult studies. In good aspect to Venus, it makes one musical and talented. Adaptability is a striking feature. Mercury makes the man intellectual. If there is a Rahu or Ketu in Lagna, the native suffers a lot of nervous troubles.

Jupiter in the First House.—A magnetic personality is bestowed on the native. An optimistic spirit, jovial disposition and pleasant manners are indicated. The native will have more sons if the 5th house is not afflicted. Self-indulgence especially in regard to gluttony will affect health. If with Rahu, sins will be committed. Body will be inclined towards corpulence. Lawyers, professors, writers, theologians, etc., come under this planet. The man becomes an influential leader. Diseases may result from impure blood.

Venus in the First House.—This is a fortunate combination, more so if the ascendant happens to be Capricorn or Aquarius. The native will possess amiability and a cheerful temperament responsive to the emotional side of nature. It gives an appreciation of art. There will be craving for pleasure. Passions will be pronounced. The native will take interest in music, drama and singing. There will be a fondness for scents, flowers, etc. Those born in this sign will be admired by the opposite sex. Generally a good fortune is denoted. Fond of wife or husband, the native will have a magnetic and attractive personality. Marriage may take place early. If afflicted, it indicates discord in married life.

Saturn in the First House.—Foreign customs will be easily copied and imitated. But, if Saturn is not afflicted, there will be much consideration for the welfare or others.

Self-confidence is normally justified. Moral stability will also be marked. The disposition is calm, grave and serious. The body will be weak and emaciated. Progress in any venture will be slow but certain. There may be some aversion for responsibility. This position of Saturn makes habits inactive. Loss through negligence and lack of opportunity are possible. The same results will be noticed if the ascendant is aspected by Saturn. Misfortunes are likely in the early part of life.

Rahu in the First House.—The health will be generally unsatisfactory calling for treatment other than by medical methods. It inclines one to the occult and the serious wilfulness of nature is well marked. A hypocritical super-consciousness towards others is likely. It makes one appear rather odd and eccentric. This combination is usually bad for marriage. Rahu will generally partake of the characteristics of Saturn.

Ketu in the First House.—Psychic powers are likely. It denotes a weak constitution and an emaciated figure. Instability and deceitfulness may influence the character. Morbid imagination, strange appetites, tendency to excitability and wandering disposition become pronouncedly marked. Married life will be unhappy unless there are other favourable configurations.

Every planet is the centre of some radiating force or energy. These planetary radiations are absorbed by all the beings in the universe in proportion to their capacity. The planetary forces pass through them along the line of least resistance.

When Do Indications of the First House Fructify ?

Hindu astrology has several systems of directions, the most important of which is *Udu Dasa* or *Vimshottari,* details pertaining to the calculations of which are embodied in standard astrological works and in my *Hindu Predictive Astrology*. In this chapter we shall explain the method of timing events pertaining to the first house.

The first house indicates the body, general health, childhood and personality. In the analysis of the results of the first house, we have to consider the following carefully :—

Whether the native of the horoscope is likely to enjoy the Dasa of the ascendant lord or for that matter, the Dasa of the lord of any house in consideration. For knowing this, the longevity should be previously ascertained. If the Dasa of the ascendant lord does not begin before the commencement of Maraka period, then what are the other planets which influence the 1st house by way of occupation or location and whether the native will enjoy the Dasas of such planets? The main periods and sub-periods generally will give a delineation of the native's life. In timing events pertaining to the first bhava, note the following factors carefully :—

(*a*) Lord of the 1st house, (*b*) planet or planets aspecting the 1st house, (*c*) planet or planets posited in the 1st house, (*d*) planets aspecting the lord of the 1st house and (*e*) planet or planets in association with the lord of the 1st house. The same consideration holds good with reference to the other houses dealt with in the subsequent pages.

These five factors are capable of influencing the first (or any) house, either as lords of main periods or as lords of sub-periods. Further (1) the sub-periods whose lords influencing the first house in the major periods of whose lords also influence the 1st house, produce results predominantly of the 1st house. (2) The sub-periods whose lords are associated with the 1st house, in the major periods whose lords *are not* associated with the 1st house, will produce results pertaining to the 1st house only to *a limited extent*. The above principles can be clearly understood by the following illustration.

Chart No. 11.—*Born on 8-8-1912 A.D. at 7-35 p.m. (I.S.T.) Long. 5h. 10m. 20s. E., Lat. 13° N.*

Rahu	Moon Saturn			Saturn	Venus
Lagna	RASI	Sun	Rahu Sun	NAVAMSA	Moon Merc. Ketu
		Venus Merc. Mars	Lagna		
	Jupiter	Ketu	Jupiter	Mars	

Balance of Mars Dasa at birth : Years 6-1-6. Longevity about 75 years.

Planets who will give results of the first house in their major and sub-periods :

  (a) Lord of the first house—Saturn.
  (b) Planets aspecting the first house—Saturn, Mars, Venus and Mercury.
  (c) Planets posited in the first house—Nil.
  (d) Planets aspecting lord of the first house—Jupiter.
  (e) Planets in association with lord of the first house —the Moon.

In the horoscope illustrated above *Saturn*, Mars, Mercury, Venus, Jupiter and the Moon can influence (produce effects of the 1st house) either in their Dasas (major periods) or in their Bhuktis (minor or sub-periods).

Since the longevity is about 75 years, Mars, Jupiter, Saturn and Mercury can influence the 1st house both as major and minor lords while Venus can give the effects of first house only as minor lord.

Of the several planets having anything to do with the first house, those in which two functions (out of the 5 mentioned *supra*) are combined will be in a position to influence the house most. For example, in the above horoscope, as Saturn not only rules the ascendant but also aspects it, he will be able to *influence* the 1st house much more than the other planets. A planet is said to influence a house if it owns, occupies or aspects the said house or its lord.

Nature of the Results

The nature of the results varies with reference to each individual case.

During the main period of a planet *influencing the first house* :—(*i*) the sub-period of another influencing the 1st house, who is associated with the main lord, will produce results pertaining to the 1st house—*par excellence*.

(*ii*) The sub-period of a planet influencing the 1st house who is not associated with the main lord will produce only ordinary results pertaining to the 1st house.

(*iii*) The good or bad nature of the results depends upon whether a particular lord is benefic or malefic, whether he is favourably or unfavourably disposed towards the particular Lagna, and whether he is a Rajayogakaraka or a Maraka planet.

(*iv*) The major lord or minor lord (influencing the 1st house) will produce effects, pertaining to the 1st house *in its relation to the other houses* with which the lord may have anything to do by way of ownership, aspect, location, etc. Thus, in case of Taurus ascending with Mars posited :

Mars in his own Dasa may produce effects of the 1st house in its relation to the 7th house.

In the horoscope above illustrated let us take Mars and see what effects (in relation to the 1st house) he will produce in the course of his Dasa. At birth the balance of Mars Dasa lasts for years 6–1–6 (from 8–8–1912 to 14–9–1918). Saturn's sub-period in Mars major period lasts till about April 1915. Both the major and sub-lords are capable of influencing the 1st house. The major lord is with Venus (capable of influencing the 1st) lord of the 4th (house of mother and happiness). The native lost his mother and the happiness due to him on that account.

In general, the different planets capable of influencing the 1st house will produce the following results in the course of their periods and sub-periods.

The Sun.—The body will be heated and there will be much ill-health. Aimless travelling and no bodily happiness. Becomes immoral or/and unprincipled, unscrupulous, will be deprived of family happiness due to separation.

The Sun may be exalted, debilitated, may occupy a friendly sign, may be in his own sign and may form important yogas. These results should certainly be modified. This holds good with regard to every planet.

The Moon.—The person will enjoy bodily happiness, good health, jewels, he will command servants, all luxuries will be obtained. His fame will increase.

Mars.—Suffers from thieves and poisons, there will be eruptions all over the body, will be deprived of the happiness of mother, father, etc., if Mars is in conjunction with the 4th lord, 9th lord, etc. The mind will be worried as a result of which health will be effected.

Rahu.—The person loses his senses and friends. The body becomes emaciated. He will leave his house and travel aimlessly. All relatives become enemies.

Jupiter.—Gets riches, clothes, equipment, etc. He becomes happy. Health will become good. He will command conveniences, he will practise exercises that build up his constitution and health.

Saturn.—Reduced in health with cerebral complaints, loses his position. If with the Moon, likelihood of insanity. Becomes heterodox and irreligious. He will suffer from windy complaints. He may incur the wrath of authorities. He may incarcerated if the 8th and 6th lords join the Lagna.

Mercury.—Health comes to normal, fame will spread, education will progress, respect from those in position. His interest in occult studies will further intensify. If afflicted, there will manifest a sort of headache.

Ketu.—He will suffer from fevers and some complaints which cannot be cured by medicine. The body becomes weak and emaciated. There will be boils due to excessive heat. Reputation may also suffer. Mind will be uneasy.

Venus.—Commits sins without being able to control passions. Health will improve. Happiness will manifest. The body becomes energised.

In the sub-periods the lords will have the same influence as in the periods stated above. In this case, however, the influence of both the planets (major and minor lords) are to be compounded and the relation between them taken into account.

Generally, the following results may be anticipated in the periods and sub-periods of planets capable of influencing the first house :—

If the lord of Lagna is weak or debilitated or combust, the native will become sickly and grotesque in appearance. He becomes evil-minded, poor and infamous and will serve others. When the lord of Lagna is in the 12th in the Navamsa, the person will always be roaming about and suffers of mind and body.

There will be acquisition of wealth if Lagnadhipathi is in the 2nd with the 2nd lord. He will also acquire silver and goldware and other precious metals and stones according to the nature of the lord. He will succeed in all his attempts. The family will expand and he will have a peaceful and happy time. In spite of Lagnadhipathi being fortified as above, if he occupies 6th, 8th or 12th in the Navamsa from the sign held by the 2nd lord, there will be a lessening of the above effects.

Lord of Lagna in the 3rd with the 3rd lord, fortified: There will be birth of brothers or prosperity to them, mental peace, and connection with pleasure-loving persons of both sexes. Enmity with brothers or sorrow to them may be anticipated when Lagnadhipathi occupies 6th, 8th or 12th from the lord of the 3rd in the Navamsa.

Acquisition of vehicles, valuable clothes, cattle, houses and lands, construction of new houses, and respect from friends and relatives, acquaintance with learned men and discussions with them and formation of new friend-ships—all these will happen if Lagnadhipathi is well forti-fied and occupies the 4th with the 4th lord. He incurs enmity with his mother and near relatives and sustains accident and gets involved in legal troubles if Lagnadhi-pathi is in the 6th, 8th or 12th in the Navamsa from the 4th lord.

One will earn the grace of the ruler or the Govern-ment of the day if Lagnadhipathi is in the 5th with the 5th lord, well fortified. There will be mental peace. He will become the leader of his community. Consistent with the strength of the Lagna and 5th lords, he may become

4

either an Ambassador or a Minister, or a high Government official. There will also be birth of a son. Political prosperity may be anticipated. Quite opposite results may be anticipated if the lord of Lagna occupies the 6th, 8th or 12th from lord of the 5th in the Navamsa. There will be reverses in the political or official career of the individual.

When the lord of Lagna is in the 6th with 6th lord, one suffers from all kinds of physical ailments, wounds, enmity with rulers, failure, misunderstandings with cousins, legal troubles, poverty, wounds from weapons and physical distress. If, however, in the Navamsa, the 6th lord is debilitated and lord of Lagna is exalted, favourable results may be anticipated. The person may enter the Army. He will vanquish his enemies. He will succeed in litigation. When, however, the lord of Lagna is in the 6th, 8th or 12th in the Navamsa from the 6th lord, then favourable results will be minimised and the unfavourable results will not predominate.

When the lord of Lagna is in the 7th in conjunction with the 7th lord, the native will have pilgrimage. If unmarried, he will have marriage. When the 7th house is a movable sign, he will undertake journeys to distant countries ; if fixed, in his own country ; and if common, to foreign countries. If Lagnadhipathi is weaker than the lord of the 7th, journeys undertaken would prove profitless. When the lord of Lagna is in the 6th, 8th or 12th from the 7th lord in the Navamsa, the person will be deprived of means of livelihood, defamed and will have misunderstandings with his wife. There will be failure, loss of business and general deterioration in all his affairs.

If the lord of Lagna joins the 8th lord in the 8th, the native suffers misery and poverty. He will lead a sinful life and contract debts. He will always be thinking of evil things. When the lord of the 8th is rendered weak, the evil results are minimised. But he will resort to sinful life in a clandestine manner.

When the Lagnadhipathi joins the 9th lord in the 9th, father will be happy during the Dasa of the Lagnadhipathi. He will do righteous acts and will be devoted to his parents and elders. Contrary results may be anticipated if the Navamsa positions are adverse. He will develop atheistic tendencies. There will be litigation troubles with regard to ancestral property. When either of the lords is exalted, there will be influx of much wealth and expenditure on desirable and deserving causes.

When the lord of Lagna joins the 10th lord in the 10th, the native performs sacrifices and other religious deeds consistent with his beliefs. He will also get a good administrative or political job. He will become more theistic and wield considerable influence in high circles. If the dispositions are adverse in Navamsa, he will lose respect and will be a victim of slander and will commit sinful acts.

When the lord of Lagna joins the 11th lord in the 11th, there will be much gain from trade. The elder brother will be happy and through him the native will benefit. The nature and sources of gains will be consistent with the Karaka indications of the planets concerned. When the dispositions are adverse in Navamsa, the gains will be less. There will be misunderstandings with elder brother. The exact nature of the strength and weakness of the two lords must be cleverly balanced before coming to a decision.

When lord of Lagna joins the 12th lord in the 12th, he will lose all ancestral property. Poverty will stare him. He will roam about in exile. He will be subject to all sorts of financial difficulties. If, however, Lagnadhipathi is in

his own Navamsa, he will slightly benefit in foreign
countries, *i.e.*, he will earn some money. When the lord
of the Navamsa sign held by Lagnadhipathi is exalted in a
Chara Rasi, there will be considerable amassing of
fortune.

Thus results in the Dasa of Lagnadhipathi with this
disposition in other bhavas should be judged. When other
planets aspect Lagnadhipathi and Lagnadhipathi is
involved in other yogas--good or bad—all those peculiarities have to be considered and then a consistent conclusion drawn.

We propose to examine a number of horoscopes with
special reference to the 1st house.

Chart No. 12.—*Born on 16-10-1918 at 2-20 p.m.
(I.S.T.) Lat. 13° N., Long. 5h. 10m. 20s. E.*

	Ketu	Jupit.				Saturn Jupiter	
Moon				Rahu			Venus
	RASI				NAVAMSA		
Lagna		Sat.		Moon			Ketu
	Mars Rahu	Sun Mercury	Venus	Mars		Mercury Sun	Lagna

Balance of Rahu Dasa at birth : Years 11-8-20.

The Ascendant.—Lagna is Makara or Capricorn.
Lagna receives the aspect of no planet—good or bad.
Lagna is occupied by no planet. This is good. In the
Navamsa, Lagna is aspected by Jupiter. This is good.
Thus the ascendant is moderate in strength.

Ascendant Lord.—Lord of the Lagna Saturn is in the 8th in the sign of a bitter enemy. Saturn is aspected by the Moon, a malefic in this case. This is bad. In the Navamsa, however, Saturn is with Jupiter in the sign of Venus, an intimate friend. Hence the strength of the ascendant lord is also fairly good.

Lagna Karaka.—The Sun is the *Karaka* or indicator of body. He occupies a vargottama position but in a sign owned by an enemy. The Karaka is therefore inclining towards good.

Conclusion.—The planets mostly influencing the first house are Saturn, the Moon and Jupiter, leaving aside the *Thanukaraka* the Sun. The native will partake of the characteristics of Saturn mingled with those of the Moon and Jupiter. The head is big, face broad, mouth big, tall, lean, fair complexion, vindictive. The body will be thin and long. Health will be fairly good but occasionally she will suffer from bodily complaints. She lacks self-confidence. She is nervous. Jupiter here is a malefic capable of influencing *Lagna*. Hence, during Jupiter's Dasa she suffered considerably from ill-health.

The Ascendant.—Lagna is Thula and is aspected by no planet. The Sun, lord of 11, is in Lagna in neecha or debility. Because the Sun gets neechabhanga or cancellation of debility, Rajayoga is caused. Lagna is hemmed inbetween benefics causing Subhakarthari Yoga. In the Navamsa also Lagna is not aspected by any planet, but Lagna is hemmed inbetween Saturn and Rahu causing Papakarthari Yoga. The Lagna therefore is fairly strong on the whole.

Ascendant Lord.—Lord of Lagna Venus is in the 12th in debilitation but there is cancellation of debility. Venus is with exalted Mercury and hence good. Venus is not aspected by good or bad planets. In the Navamsa, Venus is in a friendly sign, with Saturn a malefic and aspected by Jupiter. Therefore the ascendant lord is also fairly powerful.

Chart No. 13.—*Born on 2–11–1935 at 5–20 a.m (L.M.T.) Lat. 13° N., Long. 5h. 10m. 20s. E.*

			Ketu	Sun		Ketu	
Sat.	RASI				NAVAMSA		Mars
			Venus Sat.				
Moon Mars Rahu	Jupiter	Lagna Sun	Merc. Venus	Lagna	Rahu	Moon	Merc. Jupit.

Balance of Venus Dasa at birth : Years 6–1–24.

Lagnakaraka.—The Sun is free from aspects—good or bad. He is subject to Subhakarthari Yoga and there is neechabhanga for him. In the Navamsa the Sun is aspected by Saturn (a malefic), Mercury and Jupiter. The Sun is therefore fairly powerful.

Conclusion.—The planets mostly influencing the first house are Venus, the Sun, Mercury and to a moderate extent Saturn and Jupiter (because Saturn is with Lagnadhipathi and Jupiter aspects Thanukaraka in Amsa). The native will have a fair complexion, middle-sized stature and handsome appearance. He becomes a keen observer of human nature. He is not easily amenable to reason and displays a certain amount of independent spirit. The appearance will be generally youthful. Saturn's sub-period in the major period of Venus lasts for two years from birth. During Venus Dasa Saturn Bhukti the native suffered seriously from typhoid and malarial fevers. Venus is lord of 8 also and this is bad. Moon, Mars, Rahu association denotes emotional upsets.

Chart No. 14.—*Born on 7-8-1878 at 1-30 p.m. (L.T.) Lat. 11° N., Long. 5h. 8m. 8s. E.*

Moon			Mars	Venus Rahu		Mars	
			Sun Merc. Sat. Rahu				Moon
	RASI				NAVAMSA		
Ketu				Sun			Sat.
	Lagna	Jupiter	Venus	Jupit.	Lagna		Merc. Ketu

Balance of Jupiter Dasa at birth : Year 0-2-22.

Ascendant.—No planet is found in the ascendant nor is the ascendant aspected. In the Navamsa, Lagna is aspected by lord of Lagna. Because Lagna is the same both in Rasi and Navamsa, it goes under the name of *Vargottamamsa.* Hence the Lagna is very powerful.

Ascendant Lord.—Mars is lord of Lagna and he is in the 9th house (8th Rasi). Jupiter aspects Lagnadhipathi. In the Navamsa, Mars is in Taurus and aspected by Saturn. Excepting for this feeble evil, Lagnadhipathi is indeed very strong.

Lagnakaraka.—The Sun is in the 9th with Mercury, Saturn and Rahu. In Navamsa the Sun occupies an

inimical sign but is aspected by the Moon. The Sun
therefore is moderate in strength.

Conclusion.—The planets influencing the first house
are Mars, Jupiter, the Sun, and to some extent, Saturn.
There are several yogas in this horoscope. The Sun though
found in apparent conjunction with Saturn and Rahu is
away from Saturn by about18 degrees. The harmonious
aspect in the trinity of life—Lagna, the Moon and the Sun
representing the body, mind and soul confer sound health,
sound mind and an evolved soul or ego. The position of
lord of Lagna in the 9th creates a zest for living and considerable responsibility. Tenacity of purposes and will-
power are well marked. Being frank hates anything that
savours of subterfuge. The native is sympathetic, defends
friends or dependents in the face of a million foes. Deceit
and disloyalty alone can break his heart. Sometimes he
becomes over-critical. Detests being controlled or dictated
to. This horoscope belongs to a great man who is in
intimate touch with public opinion in this part of India
and a great admirer of talent, wherever found.

Above we have illustrated three typical horoscopes in
relation to the first house. By practice alone the real art
of judging a nativity comes. Some students are gifted in
forming accurate and concise judgments. The late Prof.
B. Suryanarain Rao had immense powers of intuition
apart from a profound knowledge of the subject. There
is no right royal road by which the whole life-history can
be known intimately at a glance. If such a method did
exist then the joy of using the discriminative faculties
would be missed. In all methods of studying a man's
character, destiny, financial prosperity, occupation,
marriage, etc., there are always contradictory indications
to be taken into account. It is often a difficult task to

co-ordinate these divergent indications. A good knowledge of the subject and practical experience coupled with
the power of intuition are sure methods of overcoming
the difficulties in the way of correct prognostication. We
shall now give a number of examples to show how the
same sign ascending produces different results.

We shall now give examples in regard to each Lagna
separately.

Mesha or Aries

Lord of Lagna is Mars and he is in the 3rd in a friendly
sign aspected by Jupiter, lord of 9th and 12th and a
natural benefic. This is favourable, Venus occupies Lagna
and he is free from good or evil aspects. In the Navamsa,
Lagna is Scorpio and its lord Mars is in the 3rd. Lagna
is aspected by Jupiter. The native will partake of the
characteristics of Aries blended with those of Mars and

Chart No. 15.—*Born on 9/10-6-1891 at 3-34 a.m.
(L.T.) Lat. 18° 52' N., Long. 72° 49' E.*

Lagna Venus	Sun Rahu Mercury	Mars		Rahu	Jupiter	
Jupit.		Moon	Merc.			
	RASI	---	---	NAVAMSA		Sun Moon
		Sat.	Mars			
	Ketu			Venus	Lagna	Ketu Saturn

Balance of Saturn Dasa at birth : Years 15-6-6.

Venus. The subject is of middle stature, fair complexion,
broad temples and narrow chin. A man of independent
thinking. Self-made, he has risen to a very high position
in life after much struggle. The situation of the Sun the
Thanukaraka with Rahu is not a desirable combination.
Loves beauty, art and elegance as Venus is in Lagna.
Humane principles and a sacred idea of friendship. The
Moon being hemmed in between Mars and Saturn makes
the mind worried almost always. As both Lagna and the
Moon sign are movable signs, the subject will have wavering
mentality. He is generally apprehensive and somewhat
pessimistic.

Mark the positions of planets. Almost all are in the
12th and 2nd from each other. Lagna is not occupied by
any planet but aspected by Jupiter, the Moon and Mars.
Lagna is Vargottama and hence strong. Lord of Lagna

Chart No. 16.—*Born on 1–9–1897 at 8–15 p.m. (L.T.)
Lat. 11° N., Long. 78° 40' E.*

	Lagna			Moon	Lagna Mars Rahu	Mercury	
			Venus Ketu				
Rahu	RASI		Sun Jupit.		NAVAMSA		Sat.
	III-34						
	Saturn	Moon	Merc. Mars	Jupit.		Ketu	Sun Venus

Balance of Rahu Dasa at birth :   Years 3–8–8.

Mars aspects Lagna in Rasi and is in Lagna in the
Navamsa. In his physical characteristics, the subject is
martian. Because lord of Lagna is with Rahu in the
Navamsa, there is a blending of the influences of Rahu
and Mars. As in the previous case the subject has risen
from a humble existence. He is not as fair as the subject
of Chart No. 15. The Sun is in his own house with Jupiter.
The stature is middle and sight, sharp. The dispositions
of Lagna, the Sun and the Moon denote a stable mind
with the power to concentrate, a mind capable of resistance
and quite frank. In Chart No. 15 lord of Lagna is
aspected by Jupiter while here Mercury is exalted with
ascendant lord. The native is rather unscrupulous.

Vrishabha or Taurus
Chart No. 17.— *Born on 9–3–1864 at 11–15 a.m. (L.T.)*
Lat. 13° N. Long. 77° 33' E.

Moon	Lagna Ketu		Mars		Sun
Sun Merc.					Venus Rahu
Mars Venus	RASI		Ketu	NAVAMSA	Sat.
	III-60				
	Jupiter Rahu	Sat.	Merc.	Moon	Jupit. Lagna

Balance of Saturn Dasa at birth: Years 7–0–22.

Lagna is no doubt occupied by Ketu but Ketu is actually in the 12th bhava. Thus Lagna is free from malefic
associations. Jupiter aspects Lagna and hence it gets

fortified. In Navamsa also Jupiter is in Lagna. Lord of
Lagna Venus is in a friendly sign with exalted Mars. Hence
fairly powerful. The Sun is situated in an inimical sign
but since this happens to be a kendra he becomes strong.
In appearance, character and mental disposition the subject
reflects the characteristics of Mars and Venus. The stature
is short tending towards corpulence (Jupiter aspecting),
body squarely built, fair complexion, forehead full and
appearance, handsome. He is self-reliant. He has a lot
of endurance, latent power and energy. He is not happy
so far as children are concerned. Mark Saturn in the 5th.
The Moon is aspected by Saturn. Therefore, the native is
always worried. Compare this with Chart No. 8. The
native attained high distinction in the legal line. There
are certain similar combinations in this horoscope and
Chart No. 8. The native is a worshipper of Vishnu (lord
of Lagna in the 9th).

Mithuna or Gemini

Chart No. 18.—*Born on 12–8–1896 at 1-52 a.m. (L.T.)*
Lat. 13° 2' N., Long. 5h. 10m. 20s. E.

		Mars	Lagna	Sat. Sun Jupit. Mars	Lagna	Moon Venus Ketu	Merc.
Rahu			Sun Jupit.				
	RASI				NAVAMSA		
			Merc. Ketu Venus				
	II.98						
		Saturn	Moon		Rahu		

Balance of the Moon Dasa at birth : Years 6–0–14.

Lagna is Mithuna or Gemini. It is aspected by neither good nor bad planets. Lord of Lagna Mercury is in the third with Ketu and Venus aspected by Mars. The Sun (Thanukaraka) is with exalted Jupiter. This is the horoscope of a middle-class man. He is tall and straight in stature. Face is well developed. Lord of Lagna is also aspected in the Navamsa by Mars. In his physical features the native partakes of the characteristics of Mars, Mercury and, of course, Ketu. The subject is unassuming, simple in habits, forgiving in temperament and self-reliant. In this case the fortunes are subject to much change. There should be no contact between lord of the 1st and 6th either by way of aspect or association. Here lord of Lagna is aspected by Mars lord of the 6th and 11th. The native was once implicated in a defamation case but subsequently acquitted.

Chart No. 19.—*Born on 11–4–1880 at 10–41 a.m. (L.T.) Lat. 18° N., Long. 5h. 34m. E.*

Sun Jupiter Saturn Merc. Venus	Moon		Mars Ketu Lagna	Sun Ketu Sat.	Lagna	
	RASI				NAVAMSA	
						Venus
	III-58					
Rahu				Mars		Moon Rahu Jupit. Merc.

Balance of Venus Dasa at birth :   Years 13–3–20.

Compare this with the previous horoscope. While almost all planets are disposed in Dwirdwadasa (2nd and

12th from each other) positions in Chart No. 18, here most of the planets are concentrated in the 1st and 10th indicating the powerful nature of the horoscope. Lagna is occupied by Mars and Ketu and aspected by Rahu—not a very good combination for sound health. Lord of Lagna Mercury is in the 10th in debilitation but there is neecha-bhanga (cancellation of debility). Lord of the 5th is exalted in the 10th. Jupiter is in his own house in the 10th with the Sun. There are five planets in the 10th, a very powerful combination. The native was a great journalist and politician—moderate in views, firm in action and obliging in nature. In physical features Mars was prominent: Thin face, sanguine complexion, active, clever, inherent conversational power. Note the Moon is free from any evil associations and aspects. There are no fewer than six planets in the ascendant and midheaven. This indicates an active and rapidly moving mind fitted to

Chart No. 20.—*Born on 29-7-1909 at 6-42 a.m. (L.M.T.) Lat. 13° N., Long. 5h. 10m. 20s. E.*

Mars Sat.	Rahu		Sat.	Venus	
		Sun Merc. Lagna	Moon		Rahu
	RASI			NAVAMSA	
		Jupit. Venus	Ketu		
	Moon Ketu		Lagna	Sun Mars Jupiter	Merc.

Balance of Mercury's Dasa at birth : Years 6–8–27.

play a mighty part.   On account of the malefic aspect on the Lagna the native suffered hostile comment, criticism and opposition.

Kataka or Cancer

The Lagna is occupied by the Sun and Mercury lords of the 2nd and 3rd.   This is not very propitious.   Lord of Lagna, *viz.*, the Moon is in the 5th with Ketu—hence bad.   The Sun is with lord of the 3rd.   Lord of Lagna is aspected by Jupiter (in the Navamsa) and is hemmed in between Saturn and Ketu,— thus subject to what is called *Papakartariyoga*.   All the three factors pertaining to the first house are unfavourably disposed.   The subject is of a stout build, nervous, extremely sensitive and dark in complexion.   The conjunction of Saturn and Mars, the Moon and Ketu have spoiled the several good indications of the horoscope.   The native is unimaginative, miserly,

Chart No. 21.—*Born on 13-3-1891 at 2-30 p.m. (L.T.) Lat. 13° N., Long. 5h. 10m. 20s. E.*

Sun	Moon Mars	Rahu		Jupit.		Venus	Moon Rahu Merc.
Merc. Jupit.			Lagna				Sun
	RASI				NAVAMSA		
Venus			Sat.				Mars
	Ketu			Ketu Lagna		Saturn	

Balance of Ketu Dasa at birth : Years 2-7-10.

mean, undignified and over-cautious. The Sun and
Mercury are malefic and their situation in Lagna is not
desirable.

Compare this horoscope with the Chart No. 21. The
Lagna in Navamsa is also the same. The Lagna, in this
case, is not occupied by any planet, but is aspected by
Mars and Venus. Lord of the ascendant is in the 10th
with Mars—causing what is called *Chandramangalayoga*.
This is a good combination. The Sun is in Pisces a
friendly sign. These dispositions are anyway better than
those obtaining in the preceding horoscope. The native is
stout, middle-sized, complexion fairly good, scars all
over the body (Mars aspecting Lagna), good behaviour,
polite manners, and agreeable disposition. Note the
combinations occurring in both the horoscopes and
account for their different dispositions—mental as well as
physical—even though the ascendant is the same both in

Chart No. 22.—*Born on 23–10–1898 at 11–30 p.m.
(L.T.) Lat. 19° 10' N., Long. 4h. 59m. 28s. E.*

			Ketu	Ketu			
			Mars Lagna				
	RASI				NAVAMSA		
Moon							Moon Mars
Rahu	Venus Saturn	Sun Mercury Jupit.		Sun Merc. Sat.	Venus	Jupiter	Rahu Lagna

Balance of Mars Dasa at birth :   Years 6–1–12.

Rasi and Navamsa. It may also interest the readers to note that the wife of the subject of horoscope No. 20 was attacked by spinal T.B. from which she suffered considerably while the wife of the native of this chart suffered from partial paralysis for a considerable period.

Lagna is Cancer. Mars, a yogakaraka for this horoscope (Chart No. 22), is debilitated in the ascendant but there is neechabhanga for Mars, as Jupiter—the planet which gets exalted in Cancer—is in a quadrangular house from the Moon. Moreover Lagna is aspected by its own lord. Thus the Lagna is powerful. Coming to the lord of Lagna, he is aspected by Mars and Saturn. The first aspect is good while the second is evil. In the Navamsa again, the Moon is with Mars—a good combination. The lord of Lagna may therefore be declared as middling in strength. The Sun (Thanukaraka) is in Libra—in debilitation with Mercury and Jupiter—Mercury being evil and Jupiter good. In the Navamsa again the Sun is with two malefics —Saturn and Mercury. There is no neechabhanga for the Sun in the Rasi. Thus so far as the 1st house is concerned the Lagna is fairly strong—the lord of Lagna middling and Thanukaraka, somewhat blemished. Martian and lunar characteristics are well marked. The presence of Mars in the Lagna has produced smallpox marks on the body. Mars has given a fair ruddiness to the person, healthy constitution, a sturdy figure inclined towards corpulence and a temperament principally of heat and dryness. The Moon aspecting indicates better proportion and greater delicacy of figure. Occult tendencies are well marked. Fleshy neck, fond of wealth and responsibility, heavy gait. The mind is not at ease as Saturn and Mars aspect the Moon.

In all the three horoscopes illustrated above pertaining to Cancer rising, the peculiarity is about the physical features. The body is middle-sized and strong.

Simha or Leo

We illustrate below three horoscopes out of which the subject of Chart No. 25 has an attractive personality and presents an obvious contrast to the subject of Chart No. 23. in regard to his appearance and disposition.

In Chart No. 23, Lagna is occupied by Ketu and aspected by Rahu. Lagna is therefore weak. Lord of Lagna, *viz.*, the Sun is in Taurus an inimical sign with Mercury lord of the 2nd and 11th and the Moon. In the Navamsa the Sun is in Capricorn, an inimical sign. Thus all the three factors concerned with the 1st house are weak. The subject is lean and has a sickly constitution. He psychologically feels that there is something wrong with his health. The height is average, face oval in shape and

Chart No. 23.—*Born on 14-5-1896 at 12-16 p.m. (L.T.) Lat. 13° N., Long. 5h. 10m. 20s. E.*

Mars	Venus	Sun Moon Mercury			Saturn		Moon Ketu
Rahu			Jupit.				Mars Merc.
	RASI		Ketu Lagna	Sun	NAVAMSA		
		Saturn		Rahu		Jupiter	Venus Lagna

Balance of the Moon Dasa at birth: Years 3–3–8.

countenance, thoughtful. He possesses considerable philosophical knowledge, is a voracious reader, lacks a natural policy with ambitions remaining unfulfilled to a great part. Note most of the planets have Dwirdwadasa positions. Jupiter is exalted. The Moon's position and aspects are more fortunate than those of the Sun.

In Chart No. 24, *Lagna* is Simha and it is occupied by the Sun, its lord, and Mercury. The Lagna is aspected by Saturn. This is slightly evil. The Lagna and lord of Lagna, who of course is the Sun, are subject to the same aspect. In the Navamsa however the Sun is in Cancer with exalted Jupiter. The first house factors are fairly well disposed. The native has an attractive appearance,

Chart No. 24.—*Born on 28/29-8-1898 at 5-30 a.m. (L.T.) Lat. 16° 50' N., Long. 5h. 10m. 20s. E.*

			Mars Ketu	Moon	Ketu		
	RASI				NAVAMSA		Sun Jupit. Lagna
Moon			Sun Lagna Merc.				
Rahu	Saturn		Jupit. Venus	Saturn Mars		Rahu	Merc. Venus

Balance of the Sun Dasa at birth : Year 0-0-18.

well-built body and well-formed limbs. A dignified nature, a strong will, openly frank, of noble spirit and an ambitious and persevering nature, his passions are strong but under control. A self-made man, ordinary education, chequerred career but now well-to-do. The native is a contractor.

In Chart No. 25, no planet occupies the Lagna, but Lagna is aspected by Jupiter (lord of the 5th) and Mars a yogakaraka. Thus the *Lagna* gets strengthened. The Sun's situation in Virgo is good but his association with Venus and Saturn's aspect have weakened the Sun's strength. In his physical features, Mars and Jupiter are prominent. The native has an attractive personality, reddish eyes, large cheeks, broad face, is firm-minded, generous, candid and honourable. Both in the physical and mental dispositions, there is considerable divergence between the

Chart No. 25.—*Born on 14/13–10–1879 at 4 a.m. (L.T.) Lat. 21° 45′ N., Long. 4h. 52m. E.*

Sat.	Mars	Ketu			Ketu
Jupit.	RASI		Moon Merc. Jupit.	NAVAMSA	
		Lagna	Venus		
Rahu	Mercury	Sun Moon Venus	Sat. Rahu Lagna	Mercury	Sun

Balance of the Sun Dasa at birth : Years 2–1–18.

natives of this chart and Chart No. 23. Mars, aspect has given a fair ruddiness to the person, healthy constitution, sturdy figure while Jupiter's aspect is responsible for fair complexion, large eyes and dignified stature. The native had a chequered career, was subject to varied fortunes, once in the lap of wealth but now in ordinary circumstances.

In all the cases stated above one important factor should be borne in mind, *viz.*, the strength or otherwise of Lagna, the Sun, and of course the Moon also. A steady flow of fortune is generally assured if at least two of the three factors named above are well disposed.

Kanya or Virgo

Lagna is occupied by its own lord in exaltation with the Moon and aspected by Jupiter in debilitation. Jupiter is of course free from neecha effect. Saturn also aspects Lagna. Lagna is subject to Papakarthari Yoga as also its

Chart No. 26.—*Born on 4-9-1902 at 7-53 a.m. (L.T.) Lat. 11° N., Long. 5h. 20m. 20s. E.*

	Ketu			Merc.	Moon	Jupiter Ketu	Lagna

Ketu			Merc.	Moon	Jupiter Ketu	Lagna
	RASI	Venus Mars	Venus	NAVAMSA	
Jupit.		Sun			
Sat.	Rahu	Lagna Merc. Moon	Sat.	Rahu	Sun Mars

Balance of Moon Dasa at birth : Years 7-5-25.

lord. In the Navamsa again Mercury is subject to malefic aspects. The Sun is in his own sign but in the Navamsa his situation is unfavourable as he is with Mars, aspected by debilitated Mercury and also Saturn. The first house in general is not well fortified. Virgo is a watery sign. The native is stout, shoulders and arms rather drooping, dark hair, forehead good. He is truthful and kind, fond of learning, lacks self-confidence. He is shrewd, prudent, somewhat indolent and has a speculative turn of mind. Thanukaraka is with Mars and aspected by Saturn. Has smallpox marks all over the body. Mutual aspects between evil planets are not desirable.

Lagna is not aspected by any planet. Jupiter occupies the ascendant. Lord of Lagna is in the 9th, a friendly sign, aspected by Jupiter and Saturn. In the Navamsa the lord of Lagna Mercury is debilitated. Both in the Rasi and Navamsa the Sun is aspected by Saturn. Lagnadhipathi and the Sun are therefore middling in strength. The

Chart No. 27.—Born on 7-6-1898 at 1-35 p.m. (L.T.) Lat. 11° N., Long. 5h. 8m. 9s. E.

	Mars	Sun Mercury	Venus Ketu		Merc.	Jupiter Venus		Mars Ketu Lagna
		RASI				NAVAMSA		
Moon					Moon			Sun
Rahu	Saturn		Jupit. Lagna		Rahu	Saturn		

Balance of the Sun Dasa at birth : Years 4–2–16

Moon is aspected by Saturn. The native is stout, dark in complexion (Saturn aspecting both Lagnadhipathi and the Sun). The chest is prominent. Discriminating and emotional and very cautious regarding his own interests. Prudent, economical, diplomatic and shrewd. Since the foundation of the horoscope is strong, the general disposition is sound. He is a businessman and money-lender and is financially very sound. The appearance is not attractive, probably due to Saturn aspecting Lagnadhipathi.

Thula or Libra

Lagna is not occupied or aspected by any good or evil planets. Lord of Lagna however is in the 12th in a friendly sign with the Sun, an inimical planet. Lagnadhipathi gets strength because he is aspected by Saturn,

Chart No. 28.—*Born on 24-9-1871 at 8-40 a.m. (L.T.) Lat. 10° N., Long. 5h. 13m. 20s. E.*

			Sun Lagna	Venus Moon	Ketu	Sat.
		Rahu				
		Jupit.				
	RASI			NAVAMSA		
Moon		Merc.				Jupit.
Sat. Ketu	Mars	Lagna	Sun Venus	Mercury Rahu		Mars

Balance of Moon Dasa at birth : Years 9–8–17.

a Yogakaraka. In the Navamsa, Venus is hemmed in between the Sun and Ketu and Mars and Jupiter aspect Venus.

The subject has a fair complexion, middle-sized stature, phlegmatic constitution, handsome and youthful appearance. Though not much educated, has keen foresight. Straightforward, loves truth and honesty. The nature is upright and frank, at times very hopeful and melancholy. Appetites are keen and love of pleasure great. Attained a good position in life and retired. Mark the Dwirdwadasa positions of planets.

Vrischika or Scorpio

The ascendant is occupied by the Moon, lord of the 9th. This is a very good combination. Ascendant lord Mars is in the 11th with Rahu aspected by the Sun (lord of the 10th) and Ketu. In the Navamsa Mars is in Cancer in debility but the debilitation effect is cancelled. The Sun is in Pisces a friendly sign, but is in association with Ketu in Rasi and with Rahu in Navamsa. The ascendant

Chart No 29.—*Born on 18-3-1903 at 12 a.m. (L.T.)*
Lat. 15° 32′ N., Long. 0° 5h. E.

Sun Ketu	Venus				Venus	Saturn	
Jupit. Merc.		RASI		Lagna Merc. Jupit. Ketu		NAVAMSA	Mars
Sat.							Sun Rahu
	Lagna Moon		Mars Rahu			Moon	

Balance of Saturn Dasa at birth : Years 8-11-3.

lord and the Sun are both moderate in strength. The
subject has taken the characteristics of Mars. He has a
handsome appearance, broad eyes and thin figure. The
faculties are good and brows prominent. The disposition
is generous. A good conversationalist with a fertile
imagination and resourceful nature. The Moon is also
free from afflictions. There is much pride in the mental
disposition. The native is a businessman and is well off
in life.

In physical appearance there is considerable difference
between the native of Chart No. 30 and that of the
preceding one. Here he is inclined towards corpulence,
because Jupiter is in Lagna. The ascendant is occupied
by Mercury, Jupiter and Rahu and aspected by the Moon
and Ketu. Mercury and Jupiter are nearly 20 degrees

Chart No. 30 — *Born on 15/14-12-1899 at 5-42 a.m.
(L.T.) Lat. 10° 45' N., Long. 5h. 16m. 48s. E.*

	Moon Ketu		Rahu	Sun	Saturn	Mars
	RASI		Moon Lagna	NAVAMSA		
Sun Mars Sat. Venus	Mercury Jupiter Lagna Rahu				Mercury Venus	Jupit. Ketu

Balance of the Sun Dasa at birth : Years 1-9-18.

behind Rahu so that they are free from the effect of
Rahu's conjunction. Lagna is fully associated with benefics and thus gets considerable strength.

Lord of Lagna is in the 2nd with the Sun, Saturn
(malefics) and Venus a benefic. Lord of Lagna has also
caused a Parivarthanayoga with Jupiter. In the Navamsa
Lagnadhipathi is fairly well disposed. The Sun (Thanukaraka) is moderate in strength, because, though in a
friendly sign, is in conjunction with Mars and Saturn and
of course with Venus too. He is hemmed in between Rahu
and Saturn in the Navamsa. The health of the native is
not very good. The subject has an attractive personality,
broad face, fair complexion and is inclined towards
corpulence. He is somewhat assuming and ambitious.
Generous position, fickle-minded, possesses grit and
enterprise. The constitution is somewhat phlegmatic. In
his physical features, Jupiter is of course prominent.

In Chart No. 31, Lagna or the ascendant is hemmed
in between Saturn and Mars. This does not fortify the
ascendant.

Chart No. 31.—*Born on 21–10–1903 at 10–43 a.m.
(L.T.) Lat. 13° N., Long. 5h. 10m. 20s. E.*

Ketu			Mars Sat.		Rahu Jupiter	Merc.
Jupit.						Lagna
	RASI			NAVAMSA		
Sat.			Venus	Moon		
Lagna	Mars	Sun Moon	Merc. Rahu	Ketu Sun	Venus	

Balance of Rahu Dasa at birth :   Years 11–6–11.

Lord of Lagna Jupiter is in the 3rd again hemmed in between Ketu and Saturn thus losing strength. Venus no doubt aspects Jupiter but even this aspect is not good because Venus is lord of 6 and 11. Mars also aspects Jupiter from his own sign. This is passable. In the Navamsa again Jupiter is with Rahu aspected by three malefics Saturn, Ketu and the Sun. Jupiter is certainly weak. The Sun is debilitated in the 11th but the relieving features are, cancellation of debility and Jupiter aspecting the Sun. Added to these, all the planets are disposed in the 2nd and 12th from each other. These dispositions indicate strides in career and lack of happiness. In the disposition of physical features, the characteristics of Jupiter, Venus and Mars are blended. *The native is not inclined towards corpulence.* The face is long, thin figure but good-looking with well-proportioned features. Venus has added softness and greater delicacy, while Mars has given fair ruddiness to the personality. The body is full of hair (Saturn aspecting Jupiter in the Navamsa). The native is sympathetic and sometimes restless. Hates external show, is God-fearing, honest and free from hypocrisy, and of temperate habits. The mind is clear and quick. Manners are gentle. The native is simple, in his mode of living. He is a lover of peace. He is ardent in his affections and seldom bears malice. His sense of justice is keen. Lacks happiness.

In the Rasi, except the Sun and the Moon, almost all the planetary positions are practically the same as in the previous horoscope. The native is inclined towards corpulence and in the physical appearance, subjects of this and the preceding horoscopes show much difference. The previous horoscope belongs to a tutor while the subject of this is a barrister. The Thanukaraka Sun is in an earthy

Chart No. 32.—*Born on 2-10-1903 at 11-44 a.m. (L.T.) Lat. 6° 56' N., Long. 5h. 19m. 24s. E.*

Ketu				Saturn	Jupiter Rahu	Sun Merc.
Jupit.	RASI			NAVAMSA		Lagna
Moon Sat.		Venus				
Lagna	Mars		Sun Merc Rahu	Mars Ketu Venus		Moon

Balance of Mars Dasa at birth :   Years 4–10–8.

sign and the Lagna in Navamsa is free from any kind of aspects.

Makara or Capricorn

Chart No. 33 is a peculiar horoscope. Though six planets are concentrated in the 10th, the native is not an entity and is at present in humble circumstances. Lagna is aspected by two malefics Saturn and Mars. Lord of Lagna is neecha and is with Rahu, of course in the same sign. Lord of Lagna is aspected by debilitated Sun (lord of 8), Jupiters (lord of 3 and 12), Ketu, Mercury (lord of 6 and 9), Mars lord of 4 and 11) and Venus. In the Navamsa again Saturn is with Ketu aspected by Rahu and Mars as also Jupiter and Venus. All the three factors pertaining to the 1st house are rather unfortunately disposed. The native is tall, lean and reddish-brown in colour. The body is thin and bony. Possesses sympathy and generosity. Has good manners and puts on superior airs. He has great

Chart No. 33.—*Born on 31-10-1910 at 1-41 p.m. (I.S.T.) Lat. 13° N., Long. 5h. 10m. 20s. E.*

	Saturn Rahu				Sat. Ketu
			Sun		
Lagna	RASI		NAVAMSA		
					Moon
	Sun, Jupit. Ketu Mercury Mars Venus	Moon	Rahu Jupit. Venus	Mercury Mars	Lagna

Balance of Mars Dasa at birth : Years 5-10-17.

aspirations, is capable of much endeavour, industrious but lacks self-confidence, is nervous and weak-minded. The concentration of six planets in one sign should be carefully noted.

Kumbha or Aquarius

The subject has an uncouth and repelling appearance. Lagna is powerfully aspected by Saturn and Mars. In the Navamsa Pisces rises which is again aspected by Saturn and Mercury. On account of Navamsa Lagna, he is stout and of middle stature. Except for the physical features, the horoscope is not interesting otherwise. It will be seen that Lagna is middling in strength and lord of Lagna and the Sun are rather weak.

Chart No. 35 is the horoscope of a fortunate but self-made man. Though Lagna is hemmed in between Ketu and Saturn indicating an unsteady career, it is free from any other malefic influences. Jupiter is in Lagna. Saturn, lord of Lagna, is in his own sign. In the Navamsa also

Chart No. 34.—*Born on 28/29-3-1890 at 4-30 a.m. (L.T.) Lat. 13° N., Long. 5h. 10m. 20s.*

Sun Merc. Venus			Moon Rahu	Lagna	Moon	Jupiter Ketu	Sat.
Lagna		RASI			Venus	NAVAMSA	
Jupit.			Sat.		Mars		
Ketu	Mars					Sun Rahu		Merc.

Balance of Jupiter Dasa at birth : Years 12–11–6.

Chart No. 35.—*Born on 27/28-5-1903 at 1-19 a.m. (L.T.) Lat 9° N., Long. 5h. 10m. 48s. E.*

Ketu	Sun Moon Mercury	Venus	Mars	Lagna	Venus Sun	Jupit. Sat.
Jupit. Lagna		RASI			NAVAMSA	Rahu
Sat.			Ketu			Moon Merc.
		Mars Rahu				

Balance of Mars Dasa at birth : Years 5–10–7.

Saturn is in a friendly sign with the benefic Jupiter. The Sun of course is middling in strength. Jupiter's presence in the ascendant is a strong factor acting as an antidote for other malefic influences. The native has a forceful, imposing and attractive personality, countenance, handsome, appearance, good and disposition elegant. Jupiter has given him a fair complexion, large eyes and dignified stature. The lips are flushy, cheeks are broad and has prominent temples. He makes friends of others very soon. He is somewhat short-tempered but becomes easily subsided. The will is firm and inflexible. He has strong affections and can love with exceeding constancy. The spirits are usually buoyant, cheerful and full of geniality.

Meena or Pisces

The Lagna is no doubt well disposed as also the lord but the Moon is subject to a number of evil influences

Chart No. 36.—*Born on 26-6-1920 at 2-6 a.m. (I.S.T.) Lat. 24° 47' N., Long. 4h. 28m. E.*

Lagna	Ketu		Sun Venus	Lagna	Moon Rahu	
			Merc. Jupit.	Jupit.		
	RASI				NAVAMSA	
			Sat.	Sun Venus		Sat.
	Moon Mars Rahu				Mars Ketu	Merc.

Balance of Jupiter Dasa at birth : Years 12–11–15.

with the result the native is not mentally normal. Jupiter aspects Lagna. The native is not stout but only middle-sized. He is of course fair. Jupiter seems to be prominent so far as physical characteristics are concerned. The body is not corpulent as Saturn aspects lord of Lagna in the Navamsa.

In Chart No. 37, Lagna is occupied by Mars and Saturn aspected by the Sun and Jupiter. Lord of Lagna is in the 7th with the Sun aspected by Mars and Saturn. In the Navamsa also Jupiter is in Lagna. The native is an athlete and has a well-developed body. The native follows a double occupation. The situation of the Sun and Jupiter is important.

Chart No. 37.—*Born on 21-9-1909 at 7-9 p.m. (L.M.T) Lat. 7° N., Long. 79° 4' E.*

Mars Lagna Sat.	Rahu		Sat.		Rahu
			Sun Jupit. Moon Lagna		
	RASI			NAVAMSA	
			Venus		
	Moon Ketu	Mercury Venus	Sun Jupit.	Ketu	Mercury	Mars

Balance of Mercury Dasa at birth : Years 7–8–12.

5. Concerning the Second House

The second house signifies, family, speech, vision and financial prosperity. In judging the events regarding the second house cognisance must be taken of all the important factors referred to on page 21 while dealing with the first house : *viz.,* (*a*) The House, (*b*) Its Lord, (*c*) Its Occupants and (*d*) The Karaka or Indicator. The several yogas—good and bad—formed by the second lord or in the second house will produce their own effects. These considerations hold good in the Navamsa also. In short the second house largely but not exclusively indicates wealth.

Results of Lord of Second being Situated in Different Houses

In the First House —The native becomes no doubt wealthy but he hates his own family, lacks polite manners, becomes passionate, subservient and time-serving.

When the lord of the 2nd is in Lagna, one will earn money by his own effort, intelligence and learning or he will get inherited wealth if the 9th lord or the Sun has anything to do with this combination.

In the Second House.—Becomes proud. The native may marry twice or thrice depending upon the strength of the seventh house. He may become childless.

The position of the 2nd lord in a constellation which does not happen to be the 3rd, 5th and 7th from Janma

6

Nakshatra is highly desirable, especially if he is otherwise fortified, *i.e.*, joined with or aspected by benefics. The exaltation of the 2nd lord of his disposition in Lagna, the 4th, 5th, 7th, 9th or 10th, will fortify him to the extent of making him a yogakaraka. The native will be enabled to earn considerable fortune through business or other occupations consistent with the nature of the 2nd lord and 2nd house. Depending upon the nature of the aspects cast on the 2nd lord by malefic planets, the native will sustain losses. An affliction to the 2nd lord may also express itself in the shape of the subject not getting nutritious and delicious food, or his family and children suffering from constant diseases, or want of cordial relations between the native and his life-partner.

In the Third House.—Brave, intelligent, good-natured but depraved character. Atheistic tendencies will be rampant and he becomes addicted to luxuries. Later in life he turns out to be a miser.

When the 2nd lord in the 3rd is well fortified, he will be benefited by his sisters. He will benefit by learning fine arts, *viz.*, music and dancing. He will also indulge in propitiating Kshudra Devatas or evil spirits.

In the Fourth House.—The above results will apply in addition to the following. He will spend money for his own happiness. He will be highly frugal in dealing with money.

When the 2nd lord in the 4th is well fortified, one will earn well as an automobile dealer or agent or an agriculturist or landlord or commission agent. He will also be benefited by his maternal relations. There will be losses on this account if the 4th lord is afflicted.

In the Fifth House.—Hating family, sensual, not spending money even on children, he lacks manners and etiquette.

When the 2nd lord in the 5th is well fortified there will be unexpected acquisition of wealth through lotteries, crosswords, or the favour of rulers.

In the Sixth House.—Income and expenditure from enemies. He will suffer from defects or diseases in the anus and thighs.

Amassing of wealth by black-marketing, deceit, dissimulation and by creating misunderstandings and troubles between friends and relatives and through questionable and suspicious dealings can be anticipated if the second lord joins the 6th and is well fortified. If afflicted, he will be involved in these troubles and sentenced for such crimes as breach of trust, forgeries and perjuries.

In the Seventh House.—Likely to become a healer. Laxity of morals will mark both husband and wife. He will waste much money on the gratification of the senses.

When the second lord who joins the 7th with the 7th lord is strong there will be influx of wealth through foreign sources. The native will undertake journeys to foreign countries and do business. When the Rasi, Navamsa or the constellation held by the 2nd lord happens to be a feminine one, then he will benefit by contact with women.

In the Eighth House.—Will have very little or no happiness from wife or husband. Misunderstandings with elder brothers. Gets landed properties.

When the 2nd lord is strong, there will be influx as well as loss of wealth. Actual observation reveals that under such a combination, there will hardly be any earnings. but inherited or accumulated wealth will disappear.

In the Ninth House.—Skilful, ill-health in young age but healthy afterwards, will possess lot of wealth and become happy.

When the 2nd lord is well fortified and the 9th lord is in Lagna, the native will have good inheritance. There will also be benefits through different sources according to the nature of the sign and nakshatra held by the 2nd lord.

In the Tenth House.—Respect from elders and superiors, learned, wealthy and he earns by his own exertions.

The native will take to a number of useful avocations. He will do business or take to agriculture and also engage himself in philosophical lectures and dissertations, and thereby benefit financially. Here again, the constellation and the sign held by the 2nd lord determine the exact nature and sources of earnings. Powerful afflictions will cause loss from the very same sources.

In the Eleventh House.—Health will be bad during childhood, earns considerable wealth but becomes unscrupulous.

When well fortified, one earns by lending money or as a banker or by running a boarding house.

In the Twelfth House.—The native becomes a respectable man. In all probability he will be a government servant, and will be deprived of the happiness of elder brother.

The income will be through ecclesiastical sources. If the second lord is afflicted, he will lose money on this account.

These combinations are again of general application. The exact nature of the results should be interpreted by taking into account, the various dignities and debilities of planets connected with the second house.

The celebrated Satyacharya insists upon YUKTA VICHARYA meaning that the matter should be looked into cleverly. This means that all sources of strength and weakness of the planets should be evenly balanced before pronouncing an opinion.

Other Important Combinations

We give below some important combinations which reveal the nature of the second house in its fullness.

If the second lord is in the 2nd with evil planets or aspected by him, he will be poor. Ordinary wealth is indicated if Saturn is in the 2nd aspected by Venus. If the Moon and Mars reside in the 2nd bhava and Saturn aspects it, he suffers from a peculiar skin disease. The situation of Mercury in the 2nd with another evil planet aspected by the Moon is bad for saving money. Eevn if there is any ancestral wealth, it will be spent—rather wasted on extravagant purposes. The Sun in the 2nd without being aspected by Saturn is favourable for a steady fortune. If the lord of the 2nd is Jupiter or Jupiter resides unaspected by malefics, there will be much wealth. He loses wealth if Mercury (aspected by the Moon) contacts this combination. The Moon being placed in the 2nd and aspected by Mercury is favourable for earning money by self-exertion. If lords of the 2nd and 11th interchange their places or both are in kendras or quadrants and one aspected or joined by Mercury or Jupiter, the person will be pretty rich. He will be poor if lords of the 2nd and 3rd are in the 6th with or aspected by evil planets. One will always be indigent if lords of the 2nd and 11th remain separate without evil planets or aspected by them. Money will be spent on moral purposes when Jupiter is in the 11th house, Venus in the 2nd and its lord with benefics. If the 2nd lord is with good planets in a kendra or if the 2nd house has all the good association and aspects he will be on good terms with relatives.

One becomes a good mathematician if Mars is in the 2nd with the Moon or aspected by Mercury. The same result can be foretold if Jupiter is in the ascendant and Saturn in the 8th or if Jupiter is in a quadrant and the lord of Lagna or Mercury is exalted. The person will be an able debator if the Sun or the Moon is aspected by Jupiter or Venus.

The eye suffers if the second lord is with Venus or the subject becomes night-blind if the Sun and the Moon are in the second. A person suffers penalty or false charges are brought against him if lords of the 2nd and 11th are in the 6th, 8th or 12th, Mars in the 11th, and Rahu in the 2nd. He suffers from eye disease if the 2nd lord is in the 6th, 8th or 12th. If the 2nd lord is strong his eye-sight will be good. The eye becomes injured if lord of the 2nd joins Saturn, Mars or Gulika. Saturn in the 2nd is unfavourable for good eye-sight. Lord of the 2nd in a very weak position makes the person helpless and lead a very wretched existence.

One will stammer or become dumb if the lord of the 2nd is debilitated, is in the 2nd or 8th with evil planets.

If the lord of the 12th be in the 2nd or *vice versa*, the subject loses wealth under penalty. If lord of the 2nd occupies the 8th with malefics in debility and the Sun combines with him, losses will occur through Government executions and fines. If the lords of the 2nd and 12th remain in the 2nd or 12th and are aspected by the lord of Lagna, he loses money by offending the authorities. One will be always in debt if evil planets are in the 2nd and lord of ascendant is in the 12th, aspected or joined by lord of the 10th or 11th. If Jupiter, Venus or Mercury reside in the 2nd being elevated the person supports many men. If the 2nd lord is in elevation and occupies a kendra, if the ascendant lord is strong and if the lord of the house where the 2nd lord is, remains in a kendra, the subject will acquire a princely fortune. One acquires great wealth if lord of Lagna is in the 2nd, the 2nd lord is in the 11th or 11th lord is in Lagna.

One becomes rich in his young age if the 2nd lord is with the 10th lord aspected by the planet who is lord of the Navamsa occupied by the ascendant lord. Take a horoscope in which Aquarius is Lagna and Saturn occupies Taurus in Navamsa. Then if Jupiter (lord of 2) is with Mars (10th lord) and aspected by Venus (who is the lord of the Navamsa occupied by lord ascendant), the man earns when quite young. One will also earn well in his young age when lord of the 2nd is in the 10th aspected by either the lord of Lagna or the planet who is lord of Lagna in Navamsa. If the 2nd and 11th lords associate with the ascendant lord and occupy kendra having acquired *Kalabala* (temporal strength) then the subject earns in his middle life.

If the third house is a common sign (Gemini, Virgo, Sagittarius and Pisces) and its lord is situated there and aspected by benefics, much wealth will be earned or acquired during the Dasa of such a planet by *thousands*. This combination naturally applies to cases where only movable signs are on the ascendant. If the third happens to be a fixed sign and the above combination in respect of the lord occurs, the earnings will be by *hundreds*. A movable sign in the third with quite similar combinations enables one to earn within two hundred. Saturn or Mars, debilitated in the 11th from Arudha Lagna, give good earnings. If Arudha Lagna falls in the 11th, 4th, 5th or 7th from Lagna, then also the person becomes rich.

Various combinations are given in ancient astrological books to indicate the source and time of financial gains. The position of the lord of the 2nd is important. If the second lord is *in the first*—One earns money by his own exertions and generally by manual labour. *In the second*—Riches will be acquired without effort if the 1st and 2nd lords have exchanged their houses. *In the third*—Loss from relatives, brothers and gain from travels and journeys. *In the fourth*—Through mother, inheritance. *In the fifth*—Ancestral properties, speculation and chance games. *In the sixth*—Broker's business, loss from relatives. *In the seventh*—Gain after marriage but loss from sickness, etc., of wife. *In the eighth*—Legacies and enemies. *In the ninth*—From father, voyages and shipping. *In the tenth*—Profession, eminent people, government favours. *In the eleventh*—From different means. *In the twelfth*—Gain from servants and unscrupulous means including illegal gratifications.

Here I should like to make some observations for the information of the reader. According to Maharishi Jaimini, *Atmakaraka* (lord of soul) has an important part to play in the smooth running of one's career. Arudha Lagna and planetary dispositions in reference to it have a strong bearing on the financial status of the person. In my own humble experience, Arudha Lagna should be given as much importance as the usual Janma Lagna. Arudha Lagna is the sign arrived at by counting as many signs from lord of Lagna as lord of Lagna is removed from Lagna. Thus if Aquarius is ascendant and its lord Saturn is in the 4th (Taurus) then the 4th from Taurus, *viz.*, Leo becomes Arudha Lagna. The just or unjust means of earning depends upon the presence of benefic or malefic planets in the 11th from *Arudha Lagna*.

Poverty

Extreme poverty is caused if lord of Lagna is in the 12th with or aspected by a *Maraka* planet. The same result could be expected if there is exchange of houses between 1st and 6th lords—either of these remaining with or aspected by a Maraka planet (see page 14). If malefics —not owning the 9th and 10th—are in the ascendant in company with or aspected by a Maraka, the man will be extremely poor.

If Lagna is occupied by Saturn and hemmed in between malefics, fortune will be destroyed. Jupiter's aspect or association will however counteract the evil indication. If Lagna is a movable sign occupied by Saturn or Ketu and hemmed in between malefics, not only poverty is caused but the body will be deformed. If either the 6th, 8th or 12th from Lagna becomes Arudha, the man will suffer poverty.

Planets in the Second House

The Sun.—This is not quite a favourable situation. Losses will occur by offending the authorities. He will have a diseased face. He will obtain money by industrious effort. The nature of the income depends on the nature of the sign. He will be stubborn and peevish.

The Moon.—He will have a large family and will enjoy much happiness. Money will also be obtained through females. The financial position will be somewhat variable, will have a fair complexion. Dhundiraja, a noted astrological writer of yore, says that when the Moon is in the 2nd house, the native will be reserved and not much sociable, squint eyed and much admired.

Mars.—Becomes quarrelsome. Good earning powers but usually miserly. Much money is accumulated. A good conversationalist. He will befriend evil-minded persons, be unsympathetic and pick up quarrels with all.

Mercury.—Learned in religious and philosophical lore. Denotes gain by lecturing, business and commercial affairs. Becomes rich. Highly intelligent. He spends money on charities and moral purposes. Clever in earning money and careful and thrifty.

Jupiter.—Becomes a poet, a great writer, astrologer or even a scientist. Increases the chances for success. He accumulates fortune, good wife and family surroundings. He will not quarrel with others. Money will be acquired through things indicated by the signs ruled by Jupiter.

Venus.—Large family. Money usually comes readily by favours from others. Eats good food, possesses conveyances. Handsome appearance, skilful and pleasant, will marry a good wife or husband. Health and wealth are indicated in a large measure.

Saturn.—Saturn, unless the second is Libra, Capricorn or Aquarius, tends to make earning an uphill struggle. Much work with little gain. Harsh speech, unsocial, sorrowful and roaming about aimlessly the person comes across many opportunities but seldom takes advantage of them. In family life he will be unhappy. He will gain by dealing with metals, storage, mines, labour, etc. He will be unpopular.

Rahu.—Peevish, diseased face, friction in family life, danger to eye-sight. Financial affairs uncertain unless other favourable combinations occur. If Jupiter aspects the second house, then earnings will be good. Money is gained through friends and business.

Ketu.—Bad speaker. Loss through fraud and deception. There will be liability in financial affairs. Success in spiritualism, navigation, mystical arts, hospital, etc., may be expected.

Time of Fructification of the Results of the Second House

In timing events pertaining to the second house note the following factors :—

(a) Lord of the 2nd house, (b) planet or planets aspecting the 2nd house, (c) planet or planets posited in the 2nd house, (d) planets aspecting lord of the 2nd, (e) planet or planets in association with lord of the 2nd, and (f) lord of the 2nd from the Moon.

The factors mentioned above may influence the 2nd house either as lords of main periods or as lords of sub-periods. (1) The sub-periods of planets capable of influencing the 2nd house in the major periods of those who are also capable of influencing the 2nd house produce results pertaining to the 2nd house *par excellence*. (2) The sub-periods of planets associated with the 2nd house in the major periods, whose lords are not associated with the 2nd

Chart No. 38.—*Born on 20/21-10-1893, at 4-1 a.m. (L.T.) Lat. 13° N., Long. 5h. 10m. 20s. E.*

Rahu	Jupiter		Rahu Jupit.	Mercury	Mars
			Lagna		
	RASI			NAVAMSA	
Moon					Venus
	Venus	Sun Mercury	Lagna Mars Sat. Ketu	Sun	Moon Sat. Ketu

Balance of Mars Dasa at birth :   Years 4-2-14.

house, will produce results pertaining to the 2nd house only to a limited extent. Likewise, the sub-periods whose lords are not associated with the 2nd house, in the major periods whose lords are associated with the 2nd, will produce effects pertaining to the 2nd house only to a feeble extent.

(*a*) Lord of the 2nd house—Venus. (*b*) Planets aspecting the 2nd house—nil. (*c*) Planets posited in the 2nd—Mercury and the Sun. (*d*) Planets aspecting lord of the 2nd—Jupiter. (*e*) Planets in association with the 2nd lord—nil. (*f*) Lord of the 2nd from the Moon—Saturn. *Venus*, Saturn, Jupiter, Mercury and the Sun can influence the 2nd house (produce effects of the 2nd house) either in their Dasas or Bhuktis. Venus is capable of producing the effects of the 2nd house much more than the other planets. The sub-period of Venus in the major period of Saturn is an important one in the life of this native from a financial viewpoint. He was appointed the Speaker in a leading Indian State.

Nature of the Results

The exact nature of the results that a planet, capable of influencing the 2nd house, can produce in its Dasa its or Bhukti depends upon its other ownership, aspect and location. The general principles enunciated in regard to the 1st house lord hold equally good for the 2nd house too. In general the following results (pertaining to the second house) are likely in the course of their Dasas and Bhuktis. *Sun*—Ill-health and expenses on that account, destruction of property and cattle, bad luck in general, quarrels and litigation troubles. *Moon*—Access to wealth and good earnings, family happiness, fame, increase of property and gains in all undertakings. *Mars*—Comforts and happiness, favours from superiors and men in position and increase of fame. *Rahu*—Destruction of the indications of the 2nd house, quarrels, litigation troubles and expenses on courts, offending the authorities and loss through them. *Jupiter*—In general financial position will improve. Any eye troubles, etc., will disappear. *Saturn*— Lot of expense, eye disease, family misunderstandings, quarrels with wife and worry. Financial prosperity should be predicted if Saturn is a Yogakaraka by ownership or otherwise. *Mercury*—Nervous troubles, paralytic attacks, etc., if Mercury in the 2nd is aspected by the evil planets. Otherwise pleasant results will manifest. Debits if any will be liquidated. Earnings will be good and family prosperity will be ensured. *Ketu*—Loss of wealth by theft, fire, litigation and gambling, eye-sore and diseases affecting the sight, disturbance from native's place, running into debts and extreme worry. *Venus*—Power, influence, financial prosperity and great success.

Generally the following results are likely to happen during the Dasa of the lord of the 2nd house :—

When he is well fortified and occupies the 2nd house, thd person becomes famous and wealthy. There will be no acquisition of wealth if the lord of Lagna is weak. When the 2nd lord is in the 6th, 8th or 12th in Navamsa, there will be fame but no wealth. Depending upon the other lordship of the second lord and his affliction, the native may die or separate from his wife.

There will be prosperity and improvement in financial matters if the 2nd lord joins the 3rd lord in the 3rd house. Younger brothers will become helpful financially and otherwise. If a musician, he will gain fame and money. There will be neither losses nor gains if the 2nd lord is weak. If the second lord is in the 6th, 8th or 12th from the 5th lord in Navamsa, quite the opposite results will happen.

There will be acquisition of lands, cars, houses and financial advantages through literary and intellectual activities if the 2nd lord is in the 4th with the 4th lord. Unexpected wealth may come in mining, lotteries, competitions and unexpected sources. He may also inherit some property from mother or maternal grandfather. None of the above benefits will accrue if the 2nd lord is in an unfavourable Navamsa disposition from the 4th lord. Venus as 2nd lord, joined by Rahu, or Mars as 2nd lord, joined by Saturn, indicate during their Dasa or Bhukti, that the wife (or husband) will go astray. When the lord of the 2nd is in the 5th with the 5th lord, children will prosper and the native gets their help and financial assistance. He will engage himself in intellectual persuits which will prove financially beneficial.

The native's maternal uncles will have great prosperity in the Dasa of the lord of the 2nd in conjunction with the 6th lord in the 6th. The native will incur the enmity of moneyed people. If 2nd lord is strong, he will acquire wealth as a physician. If Mars joins the combination, he will acquire stolen property, or he will earn through litigation or questionable means.

When the lord of the 2nd is in the 7th in conjunction with the 7th lord, he will get good dowry or property from father-in-law. When the 7th lord has maraka power, then death of the native or his wife may happen in this Dasa. Acquisition of wealth should be predicted only when there are other strong Dhana Yogas and not otherwise.

One gets involved in huge debts if the 2nd lord joins the 8th with the 8th lord. He will be unable to pay off the debts in spite of efforts. There is danger of wife's death or she may bring disrepute to the family. He will have sorrow, affliction of mind and a miserable existence. These evil results should be anticipated if the 2nd lord is in the 6th, 8th or 12th from the 8th lord in the Navamsa. When the 8th lord is weak, the native will roam about aimlessly.

Immense wealth will flow in when the 2nd lord joins the 9th lord in the 9th. Father will have very good fortune The native earns righteously. He will cultivate the friendship of learned men and will have the opportunity of holding intellectual discussions with them.

When the 2nd lord occupies the 10th with the 10th lord and the lord of Lagna is involved in a Rajayoga, it will definitely manifest in the Dasa of the 2nd lord. He will secure a high political or administrative position and emoluments consistent with the high office. If the planets involved are malefics, he will abuse his position and cause pain to others. He will extort money by way of bribes. A businessman, having the above combination, will earn huge profits in the course of this Dasa. When the 2nd lord is in the 6th, 8th or 12th from the 10th lord in the Navamsa, contrary results will happen. He may become a diplomat well versed in intrigue and hypocrisy. There will be huge gains through sources indicated by the karaka nature of the 11th lord. When he joins the 11th lord in the 11th, happy relations will develop with elder brother. Malefic Navamsa positions indicate reversals and losses.

When the 2nd lord is in the 12th with the 12th lord, there will be huge losses through sources indicated by the karaka nature of the 12th lord. When both the 2nd and 12th lords are rendered weak, the losses will be small. No losses should be predicted when the 2nd lord is unfavourably disposed from the 12th lord in the Navamsa.

Apart from financial losses, domestic affairs take an unfortunate turn.

When the 2nd lord is in Lagna with the lord of Lagna, the native will beget children during the Dasa of the 2nd lord. He will become famous and rich and engage himself in charitable work. If the 2nd lord is weak, he will have meagre earnings.

In the matter of predicting Dasa results, one should carefully consider the position of the 2nd lord and the planet in question, not only in Rasi but in the Navamsa also. There should be a balanced weighing of the favourable influences.

Financial prosperity may be predicted in the following periods and sub-periods :—

(a) Lords of the 2nd and 5th or 2nd and 11th if they have mutually exchanged places. (b) Lords of the 5th and 9th if they are in the 5th and 9th respectively. (c) If the lord of the 2nd is associated with the 12th lord, then in the course of the Dasa of the 2nd lord, financial prosperity will be ordinary.

If the lords of Lagna, 4th and 9th are in the 8th, then the subject will suffer financial losses during their Dasas and Bhuktis. If the 5th lord is in the 8th or *vice versa*, both these lords will produce financial losses during their Dasas and Bhuktis.

Let us study a few typical examples in relation to the 2nd house :—

The Second House.—The second is Aries. Ketu is there aspected by Rahu. The second is hemmed in between two malefics the Sun and Saturn causing *Papakarthari Yoga.* This is bad. In the Navamsa, the second is aspected by the Moon.

The Second Lord.—Mars is the 2nd lord and he is in the 12th with Mercury lord of 4th and 7th. Lord of the 2nd is also aspected by Saturn.

Chart No. 39.—*Born on 24–3–1883 at 6 a.m. (L.T.) Lat. 13° N., Long. 5h. 10m. 20s. E.*

Sun Lagna	Ketu	Saturn	Jupit.		Mars	Mercury Rahu	Moon	
Merc. Mars		RASI				NAVAMSA		
Venus					Sat.			
	Rahu	Moon				Lagna Sun Jupiter Ketu	Venus	

Balance of the Moon Dasa at birth: Years 6–0–0.

From the Moon, the 2nd is occupied by Rahu. Lagnadhipati aspecting the 2nd lord is not conducive to good eye-sight in later life. *Netrakaraka* (lord of eyes) is hemmed in-between Mars and Mercury on one side and Ketu on the other. Jupiter aspects Mars lord of the 2nd. In the Navamsa, Jupiter is with Ketu and Saturn aspects Lagna. On account of all these combinations, the native lost his eye-sight in the sub-period of Rahu within the major period of Jupiter.

The Second House.—The second house in Chart No. 40 contains four planets the Sun, the Moon, Mars and Mercury. The position of Mars in the 2nd is bad. This blemish is cancelled because Mars is in his own house.

7

The Moon is debilitated, but even this evil effect is cancelled as Jupiter in exaltation aspects this combination. The second house therefore is very strongly situated.

Chart No. 40.—*Born on 13/14-12-1895 at 3-5 a.m. (G.M.T.) Lat. 52° 51' N., Long. 0-30 E.*

				Rahu Merc. Sun		Saturn	
Rahu			Jupit.	Venus			
	RASI				NAVAMSA		Moon
			Ketu				
	Moon Mars Sun Merc.	Lagna Venus Saturn		Jupit. Lagna		Mars	Ketu

Balance of Saturn Dasa at birth :   Years 18-2-18.

The Second Lord.—As the 2nd lord is in his own house with Mercury lord of the 9th, he is strong. Exalted Jupiter aspects Mars. In the Navamsa also Mars is free from evil aspects or associations.

Lord of Wealth.—(Dhanakaraka).—Jupiter is exalted and aspects the 2nd house and is in the 9th from the 2nd and 10th from the Lagna. Jupiter in his turn is aspected by exalted Saturn who is a Yogakaraka for this horoscope.

Because all the three factors connected with the second house are strong and well fortified, there are indications of immense wealth. The planets mostly influencing the second house are *Mars, Mereury, the Moon, the Sun and Jupiter* and *Ketu* (because Ketu must give the result of the Sun.

Ketu must give the results of the Sun, lord of the 11th (gain). Mercury is lord of the 9th (fortune) and is in the 2nd. In Ketu Dasa, Mercury's Bhukti, the subject inherited an empire.

The Second House.—In Chart No. 41 there is an excellent combination in the second as the Sun (lord of the 9), Mercury (lord of the 7 and the 10) and Mars (lord of the 5) are posited, A Rajayoga is caused. The second house is strong.

Chart No. 41.—*Born on 3/4-2-1900 at 4-00 a.m. (L.T.) Lat. 23° N., Long. 91° 30' E.*

	Ketu				Venus	Mars Sat. Moon
Venus Moon			Rahu			Sun Merc. Lagna
Sun Mars Merc.	RASI			NAVAMSA		Ketu
Sat. Lagna	Jupiter Rahu			Jupiter		

Balance of Jupiter Dasa at birth : Years 5–5–2.

The Second Lord.—The second lord Saturn is in the Lagna and is subject to no aspects, good or bad. In the Navamsa Saturn is in Gemini with Mars and the Moon. The second lord is therefore moderately powerful.

Lord of Wealth.—Jupiter lord of Lagna is in the 12th with Rahu. But from the Moon, Jupiter is lord of the 2nd and is in the 10th with Rahu. Jupiter is neither too powerful nor too weak.

Conclusion.—There are some important yogas in this horoscope which we are not considering in this example as in order to examine their presence one should have a good knowledge of astrology. Jupiter is in Vargottama. The subject is quite well off in life and enjoys a monthly salary of Rs. 1,500. The presence of three planets in the 2nd is the most important combination in this horoscope. There is a Rajayoga formed here as Mars is lord of the 5th and Mercury, lord of the 10 and the 7. *Saturn, Mercury*, Mars, the Sun and the Moon will considerably influence the second house. Mercury's period was responsible for improving the finances to a considerable extent.

Chart No. 42.—*Born on 3-7-1909   at 9-14 p.m. (L.T.) Lat. 13° N., Long. 5h. 10m. 20s. E.*

Sat.	Mercury Rahu	Sun	Sun Sat.		Mars	
Mars		Venus	Ketu			
	RASI			NAVAMSA		Rahu Venus
Lagna		Jupit.				
Moon	Ketu				Moon	Lagna Merc. Jupit.

Balance of Venus Dasa at birth : Years 9-4-20.

The Second House.—Mars is in the 2nd in Chart No. 42. Jupiter lord of the 3rd and the 12th aspects the second. Both are bad.

The Second Lord.—Lord of the 2nd is in the 3rd, This is bad for finance. In the Navamsa, Saturn is in the 7th with a bitter enemy.

Lord of Wealth.—Jupiter is in the 8th from Lagna and aspected by Mars.

Conclusion.—Almost all the planets have what is called Dwirdwadasa dispositions (being in the 12th and 2nd from each other). This is an unfavourable combination which always retards success in life. Saturn's sub-period in Mars Dasa was a bit favourable from the financial point of view. The horoscope is that of an ordinary man, drawing about Rs. 50 to 60 a month.

Chart No. 43.—*Born on 24-8-1890 at 8-44 p.m. (L.T.) Lat. 12° 20′ N., Long. 76° 38′ E.*

Lagna	Rahu		Ketu	Jupiter	Sun
			Moon Merc. Mars		
Jupit.	RASI II.31	Sun Sat.	NAVAMSA		Venus Sat.
	Moon Mars Ketu	Merc. Venus		Lagna	Rahu

Balance of Mercury Dasa at birth : Years 5–10–25.

The Second House.—In Chart No. 43, Aries is the 2nd house. It is not aspected by any planet—good or bad. Hence it is fairly strong.

The Second Lord.—Mars is the lord of the 2nd and he is in the 9th from Lagna in his own sign. This is a fortunate combination. In the Navamsa Mars is in the 4th with the Moon and Mercury—the association with the first planet being good and with second being bad. Lord of the second is moderately good.

Lord of Wealth.—Jupiter is debilitated in the 11th but there is a distinct cancellation of the neecha effect as Saturn owner of that house is in a quadrant from the Moon. This is a benefic yoga and results in much gain.

Conclusion.—Note lord of the 2nd and the 2nd house have no connection with the 6th or 6th lord. The subject will therefore contract no debts whatsover. The financial position will generally be sound. Mars Dasa would be particularly favourable for saving.

Chart No. 44.—*Born on 29/30-9-1888 at 4-35 a.m. (L.T.) Lat. 26° 30' N., Long. 74° 45' E.*

			Moon	Sat.	Moon	Sun	
			Sat. Rahu	Ketu			
	RASI			Mars	NAVAMSA		Rahu
Ketu			Lagna				
	Mars Jupiter	Mercury Venus	Sun	Merc. Lagna	Venus	Jupiter	

Balance of Jupiter Dasa at birth : Years 13-1-20.

Second House.—The second house is Virgo or Kanya. It is occupied by the Sun, lord of Lagna, and aspected by Saturn, lord of the 6th and the 7th. The second house is ordinarily disposed.

Second Lord.—Mercury, owning the 2nd house, is in the third with Venus in a friendly sign. Venus being lord of the 3rd and the 10th has become a malefic. The second lord has no other aspects. In the Navamsa Mercury is in the ascendant. The second lord is also ordinarily disposed.

Dhanakaraka.—Jupiter lord of the 5th is in the 4th with Mars—a Yogakaraka. This is an excellent combination.

Conclusion.— From the Moon, Saturn and Rahu are in the 2nd. Therefore while the subject earns considerable money, the situation of Saturn and Rahu makes him spend his earnings on evil purposes. Mark the *Dwirdwadasa* positions of planets both in the Rasi and Navamsa. This indicates a checkered career and sudden rise and sudden fall.

In Ketu Dasa Venus Bhukti, the native lost all fortune and made a debt of Rs. 50,000. Ketu is in the 6th (debts) while the lord of that house Saturn is in the 12th from Lagna and 2nd from the Moon. The financial crisis occurred before the close of Ketu Dasa.

The Second House.—Libra, which happens to be the second house, is free from affliction as it is neither aspected nor joined by any malefics. In the Navamsa the 2nd is aspected by Lagnadhipathi Mars. The second house is therefore fairly well disposed.

The Second Lord.—Venus owning the 2nd is in the 5th, a friendly sign, joined by the malefics Sun, lord of the 12th, the Moon lord of the 11th and Rahu. He is further aspected by the benefic Jupiter who happens to be a Kendradhipathi here. In the Navamsa the 2nd lord Venus is in the 11th, in a friendly sign aspected by Jupiter, lord of the 9th and Mars, lord of Lagna (and the 8th) and conjoined by Rahu. Venus is further aspected by Jupiter, lord of the 9th. Hence the 2nd lord is feebly strong.

Chart No. 45.—*Born on 22-1-1898 at 10-7 p.m. (L.T.) Lat. 13° 4' N., Long 80° 15' E.*

				Lagna Sun		Moon Jupit.
		Ketu	Venus Rahu			
Sun Moon Rahu Venus	RASI			NAVAMSA		Ketu
Mars Merc.	Saturn	Lagna Jupit.	Sat.	Mars		Merc.

Balance of the Moon Dasa at birth : Years 4-8-21.

Dhanakaraka.—His disposition in Lagna and in the 9th from the Moon renders him fairly strong.

Conclusion.—From the Moon, Saturn, lord of the 2nd, is in the 11th. This coupled with the fairly good disposition of the 2nd lord who happens to be Yogakaraka from the Moon renders the financial position of the native quite favourable. It may be noted that during Saturn Dasa he became an Under-Secretary to the Central Government before retiring, enjoying a monthly salary of over Rs. 1000/- a month.

On page 9 reference is made to Yogakaraka or planets producing or causing special yogas. Since I have devoted a separate book* to the discussion of yogas, I shall make a few remarks here with special reference to wealth and property.

------

* *Three Hundred Important Combinations* by Dr. B. V. Raman.

Careful study and examination of a number of horoscopes have led me to the conclusion that *Chandramangala Yoga* has a great bearing on the financial status of a person. Even Varahamihira has not attached much significance to this yoga. According to him, the Moon–Mars combination results in making the man earn money by unscrupulous means. In actual practice, however, it is found that where the Moon and Mars are dignified by being situated in Taurus and Scorpio or in Cancer and Capricorn, the earnings have always been through over board means. Under the first circumstance above referred to, the Moon will be exalted and Mars in his *own sign*, while under the second circumstance, the reverse holds good, *viz.*, the Moon will be in his own house while Mars will occupy his place of exaltation. Here again the combination can be productive of good, provided it occurs either in the 2nd, 9th, 10th or in the 11th. The nature of results depends also on the nature of ownership of the planets causing the yoga. If Libra is Lagna and the combination occurs in Cancer, the effects to be produced will be predominantly those of the 2nd and 11th houses. Similarly for persons born in Cancer and Leo *Chandramangala Yoga* occurring in Scorpio or Taurus is also highly beneficial. The Moon and Mars should be in conjunction or in mutual aspect for the production of yoga. Except where the Moon and Mars are debilitated without *Neechabhanga* (cancellation of debility) *Chandramangala Yoga* generally produces bright results so far as finances are concerned, the exact nature of the effects depending on the position of the yoga as reckoned from the ascendant.

In Chart No. 46 the second house is occupied by Saturn and aspected by Jupiter, lord of the 6th and 9th. The second lord, the Sun, is in the 7th in an inimical sign. The second house is, therefore, ordinarily situated.

Chart No. 46.—*Born on 30-1-1891 at 7-0 p.m. (L.T.)*
Lat. 13° N., Long. 5h. 10m. 20s. E.

Mars	Rahu		Venus	Sun Moon Rahu
Jupit.		Lagna		
	RASI		NAVAMSA	
Sun		Sat.		
Venus Merc.	Ketu	Moon	Merc. Ketu	Saturn Lagna	Mars Jupiter

Balance of the Moon Dasa at birth: about
Years 2-9-13.

Here Mars and the Moon are mutually aspecting.
Hence *Chandramangala Yoga* is caused. Mars is a Yogakaraka for this Lagna and the Moon, Lagnadhipathi
(ascendant lord). The situation of the Moon in the 3rd
and Mars in the 9th is also good. The yoga gains some
strength as a result of which the native is financially
sound. The Dhanakaraka is in the 8th and this disposition is rather adverse.

Chart No. 47 is another typical illustration of
Chandramangala Yoga.

The Moon–Mars combination has taken place in
Scorpio the 9th from Lagna. Mars is in his own house
and the Moon in debilitation. Because the Moon is
waxing and Mars occupies his own sign, this yoga has
received some vitality. The Dasa of Mars has been much

better than the Moon's on account of the favourable disposition of Mars.

Chart No. 47.—*Born on 24-8-1890 at 8-44 p.m. (L.T.)* Lat. 12° 20' N., Long. 76° 38" E.

Lagna	Ketu		Ketu	Jupiter	Sun
	RASI		Moon Merc. Mars	NAVAMSA	
Jupit.		Sun Sat.			Venus Sat.
	Moon Mars Rahu	Merc. Venus		Lagna	Rahu

Balance of Mercury Dasa at birth : Years 5-10-25.

The Second House.—In Chart No. 48, Virgo is the 2nd house. It is aspected by Saturn, lord of the 6th and the 7th a neutral. Hence it is moderately good.

The Second Lord.—Mercury is lord of the 2nd and he is in the 3rd with Jupiter lord of the 5th and the 8th. Mercury is in a friendly sign without any malefic aspects. In the Navamsa Mercury is in the 7th in his own house. The disposition of the 2nd lord is therefore moderately good.

Lord of Wealth.—Jupiter is the lord of the 5th and he is with the lord of the 2nd, but placed in an inimical sign. In the Navamsa, Jupiter happens to be Lagna lord and he is in the 5th in a friendly sign. Hence moderately good.

Conclusion.—Note the 6th lord aspects the house of finance. The Sun lord of Lagna is also in the 2nd bhava. The degree of wealth shown is not very considerable and

Chart No. 48.—*Born on 20/21–10–1887 at about 3–10 a.m. (L.M.T.) Lat. 25° 20' N., Long. 5h. 45m. 40s. E.*

			Moon	Jupiter		Merc.
		Sat. Rahu				Mars Rahu
Ketu	RASI	Mars Venus Lagna	Rahu	NAVAMSA		
	Moon	Sun Mercury Jupiter	Venus Lagna	Sun Saturn		

Balance of Mercury Dasa at birth : Years 4–2–24.

is frequently acquired by dint of hard labour. In the Navamsa, Rahu is in the 2nd while 2nd lord is in the 12th. This indicates loss due to the displeasure of the Government.

It has also been observed that Mars and the Moon in mutual kendras give rise to something like *Chandra-mangala Yoga*.

The mutual disposition of the Moon and Jupiter in kendras is known as *Gajakesari Yoga*. Here also the strength of the yoga to produce its effects rests on the nature of the situation of the Moon and Jupiter such as in exaltation, debilitation, inimical place, etc. If *Gajakesari Yoga* occurs in the 12th, 6th, or 8th from Lagna, it cannot advance the horoscopic indications for good. *Gajakesari Yoga* or for that matter any other yoga can find mani-festation in different ways. It might enhance the reputation of a person without financial promotions; it might improve the professional career but without corresponding pecuniary gains; and it might give wealth without touching the status. Here we are concerned only with the financial aspect. Naturally, if Jupiter is connected in any way with the second house, and forms Gajakesari, he is bound to make a person earn well. All these technicalities should be carefully considered by the students of astrology before venturing any predictions.

Generally speaking, the financial prospects of persons born in different Lagnas will be as stated below. The following information is collected from a study of a number of charts. These results cannot be applied blindly without considering the other combinations obtaining in the horoscope.

Aries or Meṣha

First Drekkana (0°–10°).—The fortunes are somewhat variable. There is gain through property and rural indus-tries and sometimes through marriage. The person will be frugal and cautious. He takes advantage of circum-stances to improve his lot. The important years will be 18th, 28th, 36th, 42nd, 46th and 50th.

Second Drekkana (11°–20°).—The natural tendency is no doubt to be cautious, but the person is all for money. He gives the impression of being richer than he actually is. Financially, the important years will be 20th, 24th, 29th, 36th, 47th, 56th and 61st.

Third Drekkana (21°–30°).—The subject generally takes risks in money matters and is pulled down by his enemies. He is generally fortunate in financial matters. The 21st, 25th, 31st, 34th, 36th, 42nd, 45th, 51st and 52nd years will be important.

Taurus or Vrischika

First Drekkana (1°–10°).—The native earns a lot of money, but it does not stay in his hands. Unless he takes precautions in his earlier years of life, the advanced period will be anxious. He is never frugal in financial matters. He will hardly leave anything for his children and dependants. He will get into debt and his properties will be encumbered. He is likely to lose by legal affairs and strifes. The important years will be 21st, 23rd, 31st, 42nd, 51st, 65th and 68th.

Second Drekkana (11°–20°).—The subject will be frugal and detest getting into debts. Sometimes this frugality may extend to miserliness. On account of his overcautious nature, he may miss many sound opportunities for money-making. He will steadily strengthen his financial position. He will become wealthy, provided there are no other adverse yogas. The important years will be 17th, 21st, 24th, 33rd, 50th and 55th.

Third Drekkana (21°–30°).—The subject will be unhappy so far as money is concerned. As age advances, he will become comparatively poor. He may give his money away to others or waste it in meaningless schemes. He should deal with money very carefully. Speculation is not advisable. Important years will be 18th, 22nd, 26th, 31st, 35th, 42nd, 51st and 57th years.

Gemini or Mithuna

First Drekkana (1°–10°).—The fortunes are subject to change. Women play a large part. The native will experience adversity as well as affluence. He will have control over large sums of money only after he has reached his thirties. He will have to exercise great prudence and avoid litigation. Unexpected reversals may be expected

in money matters *unless* there are other relieving yogas
or special combinations. Insurance companies, trusts,
electrical installations, aviation and such occupations will
be favourable. The most important years will be 16th,
23rd, 30th, 45th and 54th.

Second Drekkana (11°–20°).—Government service will
not be as favourable as business or other enterprises. The
subject will fail to make provision for his advanced years.
Whatever prudence he may have, he will sustain heavy
losses. If the Moon is in debility, there will be many
hitches. He should be on guard against swindlers and
imposters. Important years will be 19th, 23rd, 25th,
29th, 32nd, 36th, 43rd, 46th and 49th.

Third Drekkana (21°–30°).—The subject will earn
money by intellectual means. Speculative business is not
advisable. Some loss through litigation is indicated in
the 45th or 46th year—the exact period depending upon
the nature of the current directions. Important years will
be 24th, 29th, 33rd, 35th, 41st, 47th, 59th, 60th and 62nd.

Cancer or Kataka

First Drekkana (1°–10°).—Frugality often takes the
form of miserliness in the native. He will do many
foolish things in finance. Difficulty in acquiring wealth
is shown and frequently the inheritance is lost through
relatives or by speculation, affairs connected with children
and love attachments. At times he will meet heavy
financial losses. He is likely to gain by private enterprises. Important years will be 17th, 24th, 29th, 31st,
39th, 49th and 52nd.

Second Drekkana (11°–20°).—The native is seldom
lucky in money matters. His generous nature will be a
handicap for him to save any money. Risky investments

are not advisable. Litigation and blackmail play a large part in making him lose money. He will, however, be fortunate in certain conditions. If the Sun is exalted, that gives rise to much earning by high political appointments. Important years will be 18th, 27th, 34th, 44th, 53rd and 60th.

Third Drekkana (21°–30°).—The native will be generally careless in money matters. In advancing years, he is likely to face poverty and loss of position. He will find it difficult to manage his affairs carefully. His fortunes are subject to much change. Important years will be 19th, 26th, 33rd, 36th, 45th and 48th.

Leo or Simha

First Drekkana (1°–10°).—Wealth comes from personal merit, but financially the native will hardly be successful. He will always be in want though earnings may be good. Trading in commodities, food and clothes is also advisable. In service, there will be sudden and unexpected reverses. He may also earn money by means of astrology. Reversal of fortune may occur. Important years will be 21st, 26th, 31st, 33rd, 38th, 43rd, 50th and 54th.

Second Drekkana (11°–20°).—Much depends upon the position of Mercury in the horoscope. The native may become a good writer or journalist or he may earn money by literature and music. If in service, he is likely to earn the displeasure of his superiors. Consequently he will sustain reverses. His financial career will be moderate. After the 50th year or thereabouts, he may get access to some wealth through insurance or investments. Important years will be 23rd, 26th, 31st, 36th, 45th, 53rd, 54th, and 56th. In spite of talents, the native seldom dies rich.

Third Drekkana (21°–30°).—The native will fare better in money matters than those born in the second Drekkana. Money is earned through unexpected ways. He will succeed in contract works, shipping products and in intellectual pursuits as well. The important years will be 20th, 25th, 30th, 33rd, 38th, 43rd and 48th.

Virgo or Kanya

First Drekkana (1°–10°).—The degree of wealth shown is not considerable and is frequently acquired by dint of exertion and labour. There remains a chance of loss especially during the earlier part of life. Speculation risks should be avoided as far as possible. The subject is likely to be influenced by designing persons working for their own benefit. Reckless schemes and impulsive actions may prove ruinous. He can earn money by judicious investment, industry, business connected with toilets, perfumery, millinery, music, etc. He is also inclined to get involved in litigation. The important years will be 18th, 24th, 30th, 36th, 42nd, 49th and 55th. He can also attain success as an organiser or company promoter.

Second Drekkana (11°–20°).—The financial conditions will be much better off. He is likely to get considerable wealth. But care is necessary in matters of speculation. Generally he will be close-fisted with money. The period, Jupiter transits Scorpio, Aquarius and Cancer, will be particularly important in his financial career. He will spend money on wayward habits *unless* other favourable influences prevail. Important years will be as in the case of the First Drekkana.

Third Drekkana (21°–30°).—In affairs connected with money, the early life will be much more successful than the middle one. There will be squandering of money

8

leading to much misery. The career will be marked by many disappointments. Gambling and speculation should be avoided. Important years will be 20th, 26th, 32nd, 35th, 40th, 44th and 50th.

Libra or Thula

First Drekkana (1°-10°).—This is a peculiar sign. The subject may either become a worshipper of Mammon or he may renounce riches. This depends upon the disposition of planets in the horoscope. Financial success is likely to follow in business enterprises, legal and political occupations. He is also likely to indulge in luxury and an extravagant style of living. Large schemes of a speculative nature are, however, harmful. Important years will be 17th, 24th, 31st, 33rd, 40th, 43rd and 57th.

Second Drekkana (11°-20°).— The native will have sudden financial reverses. Money will be made through unusual methods, sometimes unscrupulous too. He will get into trouble on account of misuse of others' moneys. He will not be much attracted towards ordinary business routines. Writing will also pay him well provided Mercury is disposed favourably. He may spend money in unusual ways. The important years will be 15th, 22nd, 24th, 29th, 31st, 36th, 42nd, 44th, and 51st.

Third Drekkana (21°-30°).—The financial disposition of the person born in the third Drekkana of Libra will be generally lucky. As hotel manager and caterer, financial success may attend him. Music and fine arts will also attract him. If in service, there will be sudden promotions. In spite of this, he will labour under disadvantages in the early years of life. The important years will be 16th, 18th, 23rd, 25th, 27th, 32nd, 39th, 46th and 53rd.

Scorpio or Vrischika

First Drekkana (1°-10°).—The monetary affairs are fraught with uncertainty but when favourable combinations obtain, the native will amass considerable quantity of money. Generally, there may be two distinct sources of income. Business enterprises, journalism and industry will make the native earn money. Extensive litigation and powerful enemies will also rise in his path. Speculation will attract him particularly though much success is not shown in it. He must avoid over-reaching himself in his efforts. Stocks, shares and industry will have a special attraction for him. The important years will be 14th, 22nd, 23rd, 29th, 30th, 40th, 41st and 45th.

Second Drekkana (11°-20°).—In matters of finance, the subject will not be too prudent. He will be a dreamer but sometimes the dreams may become reality. He will also come under peculiar conditions. He may thrive well in imaginative occupations. Much depends upon the position of Jupiter in the horoscope. When he has money he will be extravagant and when he does not have it, he will adjust himself to circumstances. Important years will be 25th, 32nd, 41st, 49th, 57th and 63rd.

Third Drekkana (21°-30°).—The subject will get some good properties. Prudence and caution will mark all his dealings in matters of money. He rarely trusts people. He will lose considerable money through robbery and swindling. Important years will be 22nd, 25th, 33rd, 36th, 41st, 44th, 49th and 52nd.

Sagittarius or Dhanus

First Drekkana (1°-10°). Saturn will of course be the lord of the house of wealth. Much depends on how the subject is disposed. The nature is to rush into schemes without proper consideration. Partnership does not suit him. He will have two or more sources of income. He is liable to reversals at about the age of 32. The subject will lose money through association with fraudulent organisations. Much care is necessary in the signing of important contracts, papers, agreements and documents. Important years will be 19th, 20th, 28th, 29th, 37th, 38th, 46th and 55th.

Second Drekkana (11°–20°).—The native is more or less a rolling stone, unable to stick to any particular avocation. There will be a general feeling of uncertainty. The income will fluctuate. Even if in service, there will be many vicissitudes. Speculation and gambles should be avoided. Mining, shipping, transport, metallurgy, factory labour, etc., will suit him well. The important years will be 20th, 29th, 38th, 40th, 47th, 49th and 56th.

Third Drekkana (21°–30°).—Finances will be generally sound except in the early part of life. The subject will make money in strange and sometimes in quite odd ways. He is likely to gain by marriage. He will receive sudden legacies, but this may lead into trouble. Provided the native does not indulge in speculation, he will amass considerable wealth. Important years will be 17th, 26th, 29th, 35th, 38th, 42nd and 49th.

Capricorn or Makara

First Drekkana (1°–10°).—The wealth will be due to personal merit and, sometimes, it may be due to speculation also. The subject will have many big plans but they will seldom succeed. He should be on guard always and not overtrust others. It promises success in any legitimate business he may care to go in for. He should try plans and projects that bring him in contact with the public. Investments connected with mining, precious stones and crystals and also factories will prove favourable. Important years will be 20th, 21st, 30th, 31st, 40th, 45th and 50th.

Second Drekkana (11°–20°).—The native will have a lot of regard for money. He will spend money on purposes not worthwhile, while shirking on those that he should spend. In the latter half of life, he will become over-generous and will naturally improverish himself. In other words, he will be difficult to understand. Banking will be good as also sound investments. The important years will be 22nd, 24th, 32nd, 35th, 42nd, 45th and 50th.

Third Drekkana (21°–30°).—Undesirable friends will drain financial resources. Music, literary work, dancing and other fine arts will be suitable for those born in this Drekkana. The subject will have to exercise great caution in money matters. During his early life, he will meet with many disappointments. But after about the 40th year, he will be successful. Speculation is not advisable. Important years will be 26th, 29th, 36th, 41st, 46th, 49th and 55th.

Aquarius or Kumbha

First Drekkana (1°–10°).—Provided Jupiter is well placed, the native will never feel the want for money. His earnings will be from different sources—particularly from journalism, book publication, practice of occult arts, politics, etc. If Jupiter's disposition is adverse, the monetary success is likely to be of an uncertain nature, subject to great mutations and to serious obstacles due chiefly to relatives and hidden enemies. His generous instincts will launch him into difficulties. He should be careful and cautious if in speculation. Gain through co-operation, partnership-association as well as through marriage is also indicated. There will be a strong desire to acquire and possess wealth, but money will only be a means to an end and not an end in itself. The important years are 16th, 24th, 25th, 29th, 35th, 46th and 57th.

Second Drekkana (11°–20°).—The results given above will also apply here. The subject can make money as hotel manager, restaurant-keeper or mining engineer. He will be inclined to indulge in luxury and an extravagant form of life. He is prone to take risks in speculation but will be successful to some extent. Great opportunities will present themselves before the native. He should not go in for large schemes. He will find it difficult to work with others. Important years will be 15th, 26th, 27th, 37th, 38th, 51st, 58th, 59th and 67th.

Third Drekkana (21°–30°).—Financial conditions will not be sound. Business will generally be good and the subject will also do well in artistic lines. During the early years, he will labour under several disadvantages. He will have several reverses. He will be unsuccessful in gambles of any kind. Landed properties will bring advantageous returns. Important years will be 17th, 22nd, 26th, 33rd, 40th, 44th, 49th, 53rd, 55th and 60th.

Pisces or Meena

First Drekkana (1°–10°).—The subject will get many opportunities for amassing wealth if he can exercise control over himself. He will be generous and spend well in the first half of his life. But after his 45th year, the native will become miserly. If Mars is in the 8th house he will be inclined to wreck his good fortune getting involved in expensive litigation. He will succeed well as healer or doctor. He will be strongly inclined to speculation and will be somewhat successful in such chance games. He will find success in stocks, shares and industries. The important years will be 22nd, 24th, 29th, 34th, 38th, 41st, 49th and 56th.

Second Drekkana (11°–20°).—Health will be largely due to his own efforts. The native will follow a double occupation. He should be able to make money easily. The subject will always be craving and will never be satisfied. Later in life, he may come under uncertain conditions. Important years will be 20th, 29th, 32nd, 43rd, 47th, 55th and 61st.

Third Drekkana (21°–30°).—The native will be prudent in money matters and will hardly trust any people. He will experience losses from robbery. He will be fortunate in business connected with risk or chance. He will have many unexpected changes. He should be careful in signing documents and important papers. He can expect gain from unexpected sources. He will be successful in investments as also in public life. Important years will be 25th, 27th, 28th, 32nd, 37th, 41st, 47th, 53rd and 60th.

A New Method of Examining Financial Prospects

Grades of wealth differ. Wealth has many sections and will have to be interpreted with reference to locality, time, circumstances and other surroundings. Ordinarily, we can recognise three grades, *viz.*, aristocratic, commanding immense sums ; middle-class people, who have enough to eat, but not much to spare ; and the poorer classes who have only one meal a day and who are hard-pressed for money. To this class, of course, belong the overwhelming majority. They have no houses, no properties, no means to eke out their existence. Then, there are people, who have no doubt decent incomes, but whose burden of debts contracted by themselves or their ancestors become unbearable and who out of false notions of self-respect, social position and family tradition cannot lead simple and contented lives. Even the mediocres, who have enough to eat, can hardly meet extra expenses like marriages and other family functions. To have a clear knowledge of the combinations of planets, which produce all these various stages of financial affluence and depression, one should possess not only a good knowledge of the subject, but also vast experience. The following simple rule, culled out from an ancient astrological work, may be tested with advantage by students of astrology:

The seven planets are given the following kalas (rays) or root numbers:

Sun	30 Kalas	Jupiter	10 Kalas
Moon	16 ,,	Venus	12 ,,
Mars	6 ,,	Saturn	1 ,,
Mercury	8 ,,		

Take the lords of the 9th from Lagna and the Moon; add the root numbers of these planets. Divide the total by 12. The remainder counted from Chandra Lagna (the position of the radical Moon) goes under the name of *Special Chandra Lagna*, which for purposes of convenience, we shall call *Dhana Lagna*. If a number of benefics occupy the *Dhana Lagna*, the person will earn immense wealth. If there is only one benefic unaspected by other benefics or malefics, even then, the subject becomes highly rich. If *Dhana Lagna* is occupied by *pure malefics*, such as the Sun, Saturn or Mars, the person will have moderate wealth. If the malefic planet is in exaltation, the wealth will be moderate in the beginning but considerable later on in life. If the special *Dhana Lagna* has a benefic and a malefic, then also the person will be able to command a

iot of wealth. The same rule applies in the case of aspects.
Planets situated in this special *Dhana Lagna* or aspecting
it or situated in angles or trines from it will also give
wealth in the course of their Dasas and Bhuktis, while
those situated in 3, 6, 8 and 12 from this special *Dhana
Lagna* will destroy wealth and give unnecessary expenses
and losses.

In Chart No. 49 the lord of the 9th from the ascendant
is Venus and his root number is 12. The lord of the 9th
from the Moon is Saturn and his root number is 1. The
total is 13. Divide this by 12 and the balance is 1. One
counted from Taurus (where the radical Moon is situated)
gives Taurus as the special *Dhana Lagna*. There are two
planets here—both malefics and aspected by Jupiter. The
Moon is exalted. The native will earn well in Jupiter Dasa
as he aspects the special *Dhana Lagna*. Since Saturn is a
pure malefic, he will give better financial prospects in the
course of his Dasa. Either in the Dasa of Jupiter or

Chart No. 49.—*Born on 8-8-1912, A.D. at 7-35 p.m.
(I.S.T.) Lat. 13° 4' N., Long. 5h. 10m. 20s. E.*

Rahu	Dhana Lagna Moon Saturn			Saturn	Venus
Lagna		Sun	Rahu Sun		
	RASI		Lagna	NAVAMSA	Moon Merc. Ketu
		Mars Merc. Venus			
Jupiter		Ketu		Jupiter	Mars

Balance of Mars Dasa at birth :   Years 6-1-6.

Saturn, the Bhukti of the Moon will also prove decisively favourable from a monetary point of view. Jupiter being lord of the 8th and the 11th from special *Dhana Lagna*, his power to do good is somewhat restricted.

In Chart No. 50 the lord of the 9th from Lagna is Mars. His Kala or root number is 6 Lord of the 9th from the Moon is Jupiter and his root number is 10. Total is 16. Dividing by 12 we get as remainder 4 which counted from Cancer (where the Moon is) gives Libra as special *Dhana Lagna*. Unfortunately, Rahu is there aspected by the Sun, Mercury and Ketu. Mercury is combust and has lost his vitality. Ketu's situation has rendered these planets powerless. The presence of an incendiary planet in special *Dhana Lagna* is not desirable. This horoscope belongs to a gentleman, once an aristocrat, but now reduced to poverty, debts and mental torture.

Chart No. 50.—*Born on 15-4-1883 at 1-30 p.m. (L.T.) Lat. 30° N., Long. 70° E.*

	Sun Mercury Ketu	Saturn	Jupit.			Mercury Rahu	Lagna Venus Sun
Mars							
Venus			Moon	Sat.			
	RASI				NAVAMSA		
			Lagna				Mars
		Dhana Lagna Rahu				Jupiter	Moon Ketu

Balance of Saturn Dasa at birth : Years 6–7–24.

In Chart No. 51 the 9th lords from Lagna and the Moon are the Moon and Mars respectively. The total of their root number is 22. This divided by twelve leaves a remainder of 10 which counted from Pisces gives Sagittarius as *Special Dhana Lagna*. A pure malefic Mars aspects

Chart No. 51.—*Born on 7-8-1887 at 1-30 p.m. (L.T.) Lat. 11° N., Long. 5h. 8m. E.*

Moon		Mars	Rahu Venus				
	RASI		Sun Rahu Sat. Merc.		NAVAMSA		Moon
Ketu				Mandi Sun			Sat.
Dhana Lagna	Lagna	Jupiter	Venus	Jupit. Lagna			Merc. Ketu

Balance of Jupiter Dasa at birth :   Years 0–2–12.

Dhana Lagna. The native can command lakhs of rupees. Venus (he is exalted in Navamsa) in the 10th from *Dhana Lagna* gave immense wealth in the course of his Dasa.

6. Concerning the Third House

The third house rules brothers, sisters and relatives in general. It has governance over courage. The third is also concerned with throat, ears and father's death. In regard to brothers and sisters, the reference is generally to younger ones, *i.e.*, those born after the native.

Main Considerations

As usual the factors to be considered in analysing this house are : (*a*) The strength or otherwise of the bhava, (*b*) the karaka, (*c*) the lord and occupants. A correct appreciation of indications of the third house rests upon a careful examination of these factors.

Results of the Lord of the Third House
Being Posited in Different Houses

In the First House.—Earns livelihood by self-exertion, becomes vindictive, lean and tall body, brave and courageous, always sickly and serving others.

When well fortified he will become an expert in dancing, music and acting, and the means of livelihood will be primarily fine arts. He will earn a good name as an actor.

Second House.—This is an unfavourable position as it makes the subject rather unscrupulous unless there are other favourable combinations. He will make advances on the women and wealth of others. Likes mean deeds and is generally devoid of happiness. He is likely to lose his younger brothers.

Third House.—Brave, surrounded by friends, relatives, blessed with good children, wealthy, happy and contented.

The 3rd lord well disposed in the 3rd, 6th or 11th indicates a number of younger brothers. When the 3rd lord happens to be Mars and occupies the 3rd, then, generally, the native will lose all his younger brothers. Saturn will also give similar effects. The Sun in a similar position will kill elder brothers.

Fourth House.—If the lord of the 3rd is in the 4th, life will be happy on the whole. He becomes rich and learned. But the wife will be cruel-hearted and mean.

When the lord of the 3rd is well fortified in the 4th and the lords of Lagna and 9th are rendered weak, his brothers will survive him. He will have step-brothers if the 9th lord is strong. When Mars is weak he will lose his lands and he will have to live in others' houses. Evil results will be minimised if the 3rd house is beneficially disposed.

Fifth House.—Much pleasure will not be derived from children. Financially well off in life. Friction will prevail in the domestic life.

If the 3rd lord is in the 5th, well disposed, the native will be highly benefited by his brothers. He will carry on agricultural operations on a large scale, or he will be adopted by a rich family. He will also shine well in Government service.

Sixth House.—Hates brothers and relatives and difficulty through them. Becomes rich. Maternal relatives will suffer. Accepts illegal gratifications.

When the 3rd lord is in the 6th, well disposed, younger brother joins the Army. One of the brothers will become a successful physician. If the 6th lord also joins the 3rd, the native becomes either a sportsman, physical culturist or an athlete. When the 6th and the 3rd are both afflicted, he will suffer from diseases and be tormented by enemies and he will himself be deceitful.

Seventh House.—May incur the displeasure of rulers or authorities. Many vicissitudes in life. Much suffering in childhood. The union will be unfortunate. Danger while travelling.

When the 3rd lord is in the 7th, well fortified, there will be cordial feelings between brothers. When the 7th lord is in Lagna, one of the brothers will settle in a foreign country and he will help the native.

Eighth House.—Involvement in a criminal case or false accusations. Trouble on account of death or bequests, marriage unfortunate, career will not be smooth, victim of misfortune.

When the 3rd lord is in the 8th, he will suffer from a serious and dangerous disease and lose his younger brother.

Ninth House.—Fortune will improve after marriage. Father untrustworthy. Long journeys. Sudden and unexpected changes in life.

When the 3rd lord is in the 9th, favourably disposed, the native's brother will inherit ancestral property. The native himself will be benefited by his brother. When afflicted, the person will have misunderstandings with his father.

Tenth House.—A quarrelsome and faithless wife. The native will become rich. He will be happy and intelligent. Gain from journeys connected with profession.

When the 3rd lord is in the 10th, all the brothers will shine well and they will be helpful to him in all ways.

Eleventh House.—Not a very good combination. Earnings with effort. He becomes vindictive. The body will be unattractive and emaciated. Subservient to or dependent upon others, and liable to suffer from frequent attacks of illness.

Twelfth House.—Sorrow through relatives, gets fortune from marriage, seclusion. Great ups and downs. Unscrupulous father.

When the 3rd lord is in the 12th, the youngest brother will be a tyrant. The native becomes poor on account of him.

These results have to be adapted to suit individual cases. Though the third house exclusively denotes brothers, the 3rd lord in different situations gives different results out of which only a few may pertain to the third house. It is not easy for beginners to understand the significance of these principles properly with the result they err in predictions and bring the science into contempt and disrepute.

When the lord of the 3rd occupies beneficial nakshatras and Navamsas and is aspected by benefic planets and Mars is equally well disposed, one will be a man of character and conviction, brave and straightforward. A friendly 3rd lord occupying a Trikona from Lagna or Lagnadhipathi generally assures a family of brothers.

General Combinations

If the lord of the 3rd and the karaka for brothers (Kuja or Mars) are not placed in the 6th, 8th and 11th houses, are aspected by or conjoined with benefics and otherwise well disposed, the native will have many long-lived and well-to-do brothers. If good planets reside in 3 or aspect it, he will get many brothers. The same result may be anticipated if Mars and third house are also similarly well situated. Increase in brothers may be expected if the third lord or Mars occupies exaltation, his own house or Navamsa, or the Navamsas of benefics.

If the lord of the 3rd is an evil planet, if evil planets are in the 3rd, the native will have very few brothers. If the karaka for brothers (Mars) or lord of the 3rd is debilitated, is in combustion or with inimical planets, destruction of the indications of the 3rd house should be predicted.

If Mars and the lord of the third house are in odd signs, aspected by masculine planets, the person will have brothers. If Mars and the third house are in even signs, aspected by feminine planets, he will have sisters. Even if the third house is weak, the person will have brothers if it is associated with Mars and Jupiter.

If Jupiter is in the 11th, the person suffers worry on account of his elder brother. The elder brother, his prosperity and his adversity should be judged by a consideration of the 11th house.

The number of brothers has to be judged by measuring the number of Navamsas gained by the lord of the 3rd house, Mars, or the planets in the 3rd, whichever is powerful. Kalidasa in his *Uttara Kalamrita* suggests that the number of elder brothers should be ascertained by the number of Navamsas passed by the 11th house. The number of Navamsas (of the 3rd bhava) yet to pass indicates the younger ones.

Whether one is a coward or a courageous person can also be known from the 3rd house. If the lord of the 3rd joins debilitation and has conjunction with malefics, the person becomes unskilful and timid. If the lord of the 3rd is with the Sun, the person becomes headstrong and furious; if with the Moon, he becomes bold in mind; if with Mars, powerful and brave; with Mercury, cautious and chivalrous; with Jupiter, shrewd of mind and bold in temperament; if with Venus, the person becomes passionate and enters upon quarrels arising out of his connections with women; with Saturn, dull and stupid; with Rahu and Ketu, the person looks bold and martial outside but will have a timid heart and weak mind.

If lord of the third is with Rahu or with the lord of the house where Rahu is, then the person will have fear from reptiles. Mercury with the lord of third gives throat disease. Generally evil planets in the third give troubles connected with throat. Ear defects and deafness should also be predicted by the presence of evil planets in the 3rd house—particularly in *Dwadasamsa*.

Planets in the Third House

The Sun.—Makes the person courageous. The mind becomes resourceful and restive, successful. Bad for brothers if afflicted. Discredit through letters. Position of the Sun in the 3rd is one of the strong points in a horoscope.

The Moon.—Generally changes in occupation are indicated, fond of travelling and active minded. Wife will be fair. The subject possesses good knowledge. Rather indifferent to spiritual values of life. Subordinate to wife. Attached to children. If however the Moon is waning, cruel, miserable, impious and unscrupulous. An unfavourable position for peace of mind, if afflicted.

Mars.—This position is bad for brothers and sisters. Liability to danger and accidents by journeys. Brave, worried on account of family misunderstandings. Reckless, pioneering and unprincipled. May be troubled with ear defects or even deafness. If the house is further afflicted, it shows thoughts of suicide or violent tendencies.

9

If the third is Capricorn, Aries or Scorpio, the evil effects will be largely modified.

Mercury.—Will do good deeds for the benefit of others but he will not himself be happy. The mind is sharp. Fond of reading and study; when once he undertakes a work he does it to the finish and will never get discouraged. Tactful and diplomatic. He will befriend businessmen and merchants. He will generally be successful in trade and speculation. A number of brothers and sisters. Independent views. Liked by friends and relatives. When Mercury is afflicted the native is inclined to nervous break-down. Gain through third house affairs.

Jupiter.—This is also a good position. The mind is optimistic and philosophical. Will have many good brothers. Becomes a miser. Does not love family and children. The body gets heated and he suffers from ill-health. He may be devoid of gratitude if Jupiter is afflicted. He does not have many friends. Does not take advantage of opportunities. Adapts himself to conventionalities.

Venus.—The mental quality is good but health will be poor, lacking in vitality. He will take delight in singing, music, dancing and fine arts. Financially he will not be very successful. If Venus is afflicted, miserly, mean, poor and highly sensual. He becomes funky and interested in scandals. Brothers will be good. Not much happiness from children.

Saturn.—Brave and courageous, wealthy, loss of brothers, eccentric and cruel. Sorrow through brothers; honoured by rulers; may become head or president of local boards, municipalities, etc. He will protect many people. One peculiarity of this combination is that success attends him only after he has suffered disappointments and reverses. The tendency of the mind is towards gloom, anxiety and misgivings. The mental condition

improves with age. If Saturn is afflicted, the despondency
is likely to run into mental affliction.

Rahu.—Brave for outward appearances. Sudden and
unexpected news. The combination is generally bad for
brothers. He may incur severe criticism on account of
his views and ideas.

Ketu.—Strong and adventurous but funky. Disturbs
the mind with hallucinations.

When the Indications will Fructify

The general principles for judging the results of Dasas
and Bhuktis in reference to the 1st and 2nd houses also
hold good with reference to the 3rd. First take the house,
then the lord and finally the karaka. Planets in association with or aspecting the lord and karaka will imprint
their characteristics also. Planets occupying and aspecting
the third are also important. Thus (*a*) the 3rd lord, (*b*)
planets in association with or aspecting the third lord, (*c*)
planets situated in and aspecting the third, and (*d*) the
karaka, and the planets in association with or aspecting
karaka, may influence the third house either as lords of
main periods or as lords of sub-periods.

Consequently, the sub-periods of planets capable of
influencing the third in the major periods of those connected with the third in any one of the capacities mentioned
above will produce results pertaining to the third house
par excellence. The sub-periods of planets associated with
the third house in the major periods, whose lords are not
associated with the third house, will produce results pertaining to the third only to a limited extent. Consequently
the sub-periods of planets, not associated with the third
house in the major periods whose lords are associated, will
produce effects pertaining to the third house, to a limited
extent.

Predict birth of brothers (or sisters) during the Dasa (or Bhuktis) of the lords of the 3rd, 9th, 11th and 7th; birth of brothers may also occur in the Dasa of the lord of the third or the most powerful of the planets occupying the third.

As in reference to other bhavas, the exact nature of the results depends upon the ownership, etc., of other planets connected with the third house. The following results may be expected in the periods of the different planets when they have anything to do with the third house:—

The Sun.—Interviews with prominent men, promotions, access to comforts and rejoicings at home.

The Moon.—The native becomes more courageous, brothers will be born or they will become prosperous. Gain of money and landed properties.

Mars —One becomes weak so far as health is concerned, fame will increase. Finances will improve. If Mars is afflicted, death of a brother may occur.

Rahu.—On the whole good results will be produced. Health will improve but there may be some friction in the domestic life. Reputation and respect will increase.

Jupiter.—Brothers and sisters will be born. The subject becomes war-like. All his efforts will be crowned with success.

Saturn.—Disputes will arise with brothers. Financially the period would prove favourable. If in service, there will be promotion. Birth of children, access to jewels and new clothes and good in all respects.

Mercury.—Auspicious celebrations, redemption from debts and machinations of enemies, respect from others; weddings of brothers and purchase of jewels.

Ketu.—Enemies will be destroyed, becomes well-versed in music and dancing. Generally the period will be a favourable one.

Venus.—All uncertainties will disappear. He takes interest in music and leads a happy life.

It will be seen from the above that the Dasas of planets situated in the 3rd will generally produce good results. It is implied however that such a disposition in the 3rd house is devoid of any other malefic influences.

In general, the following results may be anticipated during the Dasa (or the Bhukti) of the third lord subject to the modification due to the other lordship, association, aspect, etc.

When the third lord is in the third, there will be birth of younger brothers (and sisters) ; prosperity will attend the existing brothers ; the next eldest will have his marriage celebrated.

When the third lord is in the fourth with the fourth lord, brothers will shine well. The subject will become the head of a political or scientific organisation and will acquire a new vehicle. If a student, he will pass in examinations. When the fourth lord is weak, there will be affliction to mother, loss of property and destruction of crops (if the native is an agriculturist). If the third lord is weak, brothers will cause unpleasantness and losses. The family will break up and brothers will separate. The man will sustain an accident by falling from a vehicle. If the third lord is in the 6th, 8th or 12th from the 4th lord in the Navamsa, then either in the sub-period of the 3rd lord or in that of the 4th lord (within the Dasa of the 3rd lord) brothers will die, the person will be deprived of his conveyance, and he will be extremely unhappy.

When the 3rd lord is in the 5th with the 5th lord, well fortified, then the native gets political power as a Minister, provided other Rajayogas function at the same time. Otherwise, his brother will get a high administrative post. Or the native will acquire fortune through divine grace. One would eke out his existence as a dependent or a servant if the third lord is weak. If the native is a musician, then there will be considerable influx of fortune generally through the grace of the rulers. He will be entirely disappointed in his hopes if the 3rd lord holds an amsa which happens to be the 6th, 8th or 12th from the Navamsa of the 5th lord.

The native's brother will become a bitter enemy during the Dasa (or Bhukti) of the 3rd lord if he joins the 6th with the 6th lord. Or both will fall seriously ill. If a benefic joins this combination, the native gets a job connected with the army. He will benefit by his maternal uncles. When the 3rd lord is afflicted, *status quo* would continue. When the lord of the 3rd is in the 6th and is *affected* (*i.e.*, associated with or aspected by) *both* the lords of the 6th and 12th, then the Dasa becomes capable of producing Rajayoga results. There will be acquisition of property, wealth and fame. If the 6th lord alone joins or aspects, then the person will suffer from ear trouble.

The native's brother will go to far-off lands, if the 3rd lord is in the 7th with the 7th lord. When both the lords are well disposed, the brother will have a happy and profitable foreign trip. If the 7th bhava falls in a Chara Rasi, the journey undertaken will be to a distant country. If the seventh house is weak, the brother will meet with sorrow and misfortune ; or he will die there. At the time this misfortune happens to the brother, the native's relations with his parents will become cordial. By carefully analysing the seventh house, one can predict second marriage for the native during this Dasa (or Bhukti).

Brother's journey, as indicated above, will not come off if the 3rd lord is in the 6th, 8th or 12th from the 7th lord in the Navamsa ; nor does any kind of misfortune befall the brother. When the 7th lord is weak, the brother will roam about in distant lands and lead a sinful life.

When the 3rd lord is in the 8th with the 8th lord, the native will suffer from ear diseases, his enemies will win and the native becomes miserable and unhappy. There will be enmity with brothers and other near relatives or death to one of the brothers. If, however, the 3rd lord is in the 8th with the 8th lord, and also has the contact of the 6th lord (either by aspect or association), the native will have financial gains. The same results can also be anticipated if the 3rd lord is in the 6th, 8th or 12th from the 8th lord in the Navamsa.

The native's brother becomes fortunate and prosperous (in the Dasa of the 3rd lord) if the 3rd lord joins the 9th house with the 9th lord. Father's property will increase and the native becomes religious. When the 9th lord is weak, misunderstandings with father will arise. When the third lord is weak, the evil results are lesssened.

When the 3rd lord is in the 10th in association with the 10th lord, the person meets with frustration and disappointments. His daily mode of life will be upset. When the 10th lord is afflicted, he will become immoral and commit sins and his brothers take to questionable means of earning money. When the 10th lord is fortified, one of the brothers attains distinction in the political field.

When the 3rd lord is in the 11th with the 11th lord, both the elder and younger brothers will have powerful Rajayogas. In case the horoscopes of the brothers show a bad period, then the evil would be mitigated. The brothers may start a new business venture in articles represented by their birth constellations. When the third

lord is weak, the elder brothers prosper and the younger
brothers suffer strokes of misfortune.

When the third is lord is weak and joins the 12th with
the 12th lord, the younger brother (next to the native) will
die   He will meet with a series of misfortunes, will have
fear from enemies, ear diseases and will have to sell or
mortgage all his jewels. There will be mental affliction also.
When the 12th house is a movable sign, brother's death
will happen in a far-off country.   When the third lord is
in Lagna with the lord of Lagna, there will be increase of
prosperity.   He will become proficient in music, becomes
self-confident and his enemies will be vanquished.   When
Lagna is a feminine sign, the native may associate with
women of questionable character and earn money through
their favours.   When Lagnadhipati is weak and otherwise
afflicted, the person's behaviour becomes scandalous in
the public eye.

When the 3rd lord is in the 2nd with the 2nd lord, the
native's brother will die. Mother will be afflicted mentally
and physically.   If the 2nd and 3rd lords are well-fortified,
then prosperity to brothers should be predicted.

In predicting results of Dasas or Bhuktis, due attention must be paid to all shades of influences covering a
particular bhava or house.   A lord is capable of conferring the results of not only the house but those due to
karaka nature of planets joining or aspecting the bhava.

The Third House.—In Chart No. 52 the third house
is Cancer and it is not occupied or aspected by any
planets, benefic or malefic.   Hence it is fairly strong.

The Third Lord.—The Moon is the third lord and he
is in the 12th with Rahu aspected by Mars and Ketu. This
is bad.   The Moon occupies a benefic Navamsa.

Chart No. 52.—*Born on 12-2-1856 at 12-21 p.m. (L.T.) Lat. 18° N., Long. 84° E.*

	Moon Rahu	Lagna	Sat.		Lagna Jupiter	Rahu	
Sun Merc. Jupit.		RASI			NAVAMSA		
Venus	Mars Ketu			Merc.	Ketu	Sun Saturn Venus Mars	Moon

Balance of Venus Dasa at birth : Years 12-3-9.

Lord of Brothers.—Mars is in the 6th with Ketu; Jupiter aspects Mars. In the Navamsa his disposition is not very good.

Conclusion.—Thus the third house is good, Mars ordinary and the third lord rather weak. The Moon, lord of the 3rd, has gained six Navamsas. The native had 6 brothers (and sisters born) out of whom three died early in life. The person was extremely resourceful, courageous, skilful, diplomatic, yet truthful.

The Third House is Taurus (Chart No. 53). Rahu occupies it. The third is aspected by the Moon, Mars and Ketu. Rahu's presence is not very auspicious.

The Third Lord.—Venus is in the 7th with exalted Mercury. Venus gets neechabhanga or cancellation of debility. Venus is aspected by Jupiter. *Mars*, Bhratru-karaka, is in the 9th in his own house.

Chart No. 53.—*Born on 24–8–18√0 at 8–44 p.m. (L.T.) Lat. 13° N., Long. 5h. 10m. 20s. E.*

Lagna		Rahu		Ketu		Jupiter	Sun
				Moon Merc. Mars			
	RASI				NAVAMSA		
Jupit.			Sun Sat.				Venus Sat.
	Moon Mars Ketu		Merc. Venus		Lagna		Rahu

Balance of Mercury Dasa at birth : Years 5–10–25.

Therefore, whilst the third house is not good, the third lord and Mars are well disposed with the result the native is blessed with a number of brothers and sisters. The third lord Venus is more powerful than the planets aspecting the third. Venus is in the 8th Navamsa—indicating the native will have 8 brothers and sisters ; out of whom (including the native) five are surviving. As the third house has more to do with the feminine planets the native will have sisters. Venus is in the 8th Navamsa— the 8th from Capricorn. In between the 1st and 8th Navamsa Mars, Jupiter and the Sun—three masculine planets—are found. Therefore the number of brothers is three and the rest, sisters.

The Third House.—Capricorn is the third and Ketu is situated there (Chart No. 54). This is aspected by the Sun, Mercury, Rahu, Saturn and Mars—all malefics.

Chart No. 54.—*Born on 7-8-1887 at 1-35 p.m. (L.T.)
Lat. 11° N., Long. 5h. 8m. E.*

Moon			Mars	Venus Rahu		Mars	
			Sun Merc. Rahu Sat.				Moon
	RASI				**NAVAMSA**		
Ketu					Sun		Sat.
	Lagna	Jupiter	Venus	Jupit.	Lagna		Merc Ketu

Balance of Jupiter Dasa at birth : Year 0-2-12.

The Third Lord.—Saturn is aspecting the 3rd and he
is in conjunction with the Sun, Mercury and Rahu. Mars
is in the 8th (9th bhava) and aspected by Jupiter. Of the
three elements, the third lord is more powerful than the
third house or Mars. The native will have brothers. The
third lord Saturn is in the 2nd Navamsa. The native will
therefore have only two brothers (including himself).

In Chart No. 55, lord of the third Venus is in the
12th with Mars who aspects the third. Saturn lord of the
6th aspects the third. Both Mars and Venus are subject
to *Papakarthari Yoga.* The native is somewhat deaf.

In Chart No. 56, the third house is aspected by
Saturn and the third lord is debilitated in the 6th. The
native is partially *deaf.*

In Chart No. 57, the third is aspected by Mars and
Venus—lord of the 12th and 6th respectively. The third
lord Moon is aspected by Saturn. From the Moon, the
third is occupied by Ketu. The native is partially deaf.

Chart No. 55.—*Born on 10-9-1889 at about sunrise. Lat. 13° N., Long. 5h. 10m. 20s. E.*

Moon		Rahu				Merc. Sat.
	RASI	Mars Venus	Rahu	NAVAMSA		Moon Jupit.
		Sun Sat. Lagna				Ketu
Ketu Jupit.		Merc.	Mars Lagna Venus	Sun		

Balance of Jupiter Dasa at birth : Years 3-0-6.

Chart No. 56.—*Born on 1-6-1895 at 11-42 p.m. (L.T.) Lat. 13° N., Long. 75° 35' E.*

	Sun	Merc. Jupit.	Jupit.		Rahu	Sun
Lagna Rahu	RASI	Mars Venus	Moon	NAVAMSA		Mars Venus
		Ketu	Sat.			
	Saturn	Moon	Merc. Lagna	Ketu		

Balance of the Sun Dasa at birth : Years 1-6-13.

Chart No. 57.—*Born on 9-3-1864 at 11-27 a.m. (L.T.) Lat. 13° N., Long. 77° 35' E.*

Moon	Ketu Lagna		Mars			Sun
Sun Merc.	RASI			NAVAMSA		Venus Rahu
Mars Venus			Ketu			Sat.
	Jupiter Rahu	Sat.	Merc.		Moon	Jupit. Lagna

Balance of Saturn Dasa at birth :   Years 7-0-22.

Thus it will be seen that in the analysis of the different bhavas great care and caution have to be applied as otherwise the results are bound to go erroneous. In the examples illustrated I have purposely refrained from taking into account the several yogas that may be present in them as I do not want the readers to get confused. One should have a good memory, ready powers of analysis and a capable mind to grasp the varied and conflicting evidence presented before his mind and draw proper and reasonable conclusions.

The Third House.—The third is a malefic sign Aries and is occupied by Ketu, an incendiary planet (Chart No. 58). It is aspected by another malefic Mars, who is the lord of the house and Jupiter, a benefic, from his own sign. The first is the bad but the second is good.

The Third Lord.—The ruler of the third is Mars, who is himself the karaka of brothers. He is in the ninth, a

Chart No. 58.—*Born on 28-8-1901 at 4-30 p.m. (L.T.) Lat. 16° 18 N., Long. 80° 41' E.*

	Ketu			Venus		Mandi Mercury Rahu	Sun
Lagna							Jupit.
	RASI				NAVAMSA		
			Sun Merc.	Moon			
Jupit. Sat.	Moon	Mars Rahu	Venus Mandi	Lagna	Mars Ketu		Sat.

Balance of Mercury Dasa at birth : Years 12–0–25.

good house and a benefic sign, but ruled by an inimical planet Venus and is posited with Rahu, an incendiary planet. In Navamsa he is in the 12th in his own house with Ketu. He is further afflicted by the powerful aspect of Saturn placed in a kendra from Lagna. Therefore the third lord is weak in the horoscope.

Karaka.—Mars is the karaka of brothers. He is therefore subject to the same afflictions as the lord.

Except for the single benefic influence of Jupiter who aspects the third house, the house as well as the lord of brothers come under severe affliction. There by the indications of the house suffer. The subject of the chart has no brothers.

The Third House.—The third is Libra, a benefic sign, and it is unoccupied by any planet. It is aspected by Jupiter and Mars from the ninth. Of the two the aspect of Mars is more powerful, as the planet is in his own

Chart No. 59.—*Born on 9-7-1928 at 8-50 a.m. (I.S.T.) Long. 77° 45' E., Lat. 9° 25' N.*

Moon	Mars Jupiter	Rahu	Venus Sun Merc.		Lagna	Sun Rahu	Venus
				Merc. Sat.			Jupit.
	RASI		Lagna		NAVAMSA		
	Saturn Ketu Mandi				Ketu		Moon Mars Mandi

Balance of Saturn Dasa at birth : Years 12–10–14.

house. The bhava suffers on this account as Mars is a natural malefic.

The Third Lord.—The lord of the third, Venus, occupies Gemini, a friendly sign and is Vargottama in the chart (Chart No. 59). This is good. But in the Rasi he is with an inimical planet Sun and has become combust. This makes him weak in the chart.

Lord of Brothers.—Mars the ruler of brothers occupies the ninth from Lagna which is his own house and is with Jupiter a natural benefic. In Navamsa he occupies a benefic but inimical sign and is placed in an evil house with Moon and Mandi. Altogether his position is fair in the chart.

Conclusion.—Though the karaka Mars is well disposed, the fact of the ruler of the third becoming combust and hence powerless, renders the third house weak. This stands against his having any brothers.

Chart No. 60.—*Born on 21–10–1896 at 6 a.m. (L.T.) Lat. 9° 58' N., Long. 78° 2' E.*

	Moon		Mars	Ketu		Sat. Merc.
			Ketu			Moon Jupit.
Rahu	RASI		—	NAVAMSA		Venus Mandi
			Jupit.			
Mandi	Venus	Lagna Sun Saturn	Merc.	Lagna Sun Mars		Rahu

Balance of Ketu Dasa at birth :   Years 0–9–14.

The Third House.—The third is Sagittarius, a benefic sign, and is occupied by Mandi and aspected by two evil planets, Mars and Saturn. This is bad. Jupiter aspects the third house from the eleventh and this somewhat mitigates the evil. But still the bhava is not sufficiently strong.

The Third Lord.—The lord of the third is Jupiter and he occupies the 11th from Lagna in Rasi and is exalted in Navamsa. This is good. But in bhava there is Jupiter Ketu association, and thus Jupiter is rendered weak. Even otherwise he is afflicted by the powerful aspect of Mars in Navamsa. As such the third lord is not sufficiently strong.

Lord of Brothers.—The lord of brothers Mars is posited in the ninth a good house, but is in the sign of an enemy. Though in a benefic Navamsa, he is with the Sun aspected by Saturn which is bad. His disposition is not very good in the chart.

Conclusion.—Though Jupiter is well-disposed in the horoscope, the karaka and the third house are subject to affliction. The native has no brothers.

Chart No 61.—*Born on 29–12–1880 at 10–10 a.m. (L.T.) Lat. 22° 35' N., Long. 88° 23' E.*

Jupit. Mandi	Saturn		Ketu	Mars	Mercury Saturn	Rahu	—
Lagna				Lagna			
	RASI				NAVAMSA		
Venus							
Sun Merc. Rahu	Moon Mars			Jupit.	Moon Ketu	Mandi	Sun Venus

Balance of Saturn Dasa at birth : Years 4–7–19.

The Third House.—The third house is Aries a malefic sign and it is occupied by an evil planet, Saturn. Though the latter is the Lagna lord, he is debilitated. This makes the house weak in Rasi. In Amsa the indications are no better as the third is occupied by debilitated Saturn. The only relieving feature is, the house is joined by Mercury and aspected by Jupiter. Still the house is not sufficiently strong.

The Third Lord.—The third lord happens to be Mars, the karaka. He is posited in a kendra and own sign but his situation in the 8th from the 3rd and with the ruler of the 6th Moon renders him weak. The planet is aspected by Jupiter from his own sign but even here it is in

10

name only as Jupiter stands in an evil house from the
bhava—the 12th. Hence the situation of the third lord is
not very good in the chart.

Lord of Brothers.—Mars being the karaka is subject
to the same influences as the third lord.

Conclusion.—The third house is subject to 'Papakarthari' Yoga in Amsa in addition to other afflictions.
The strength of the 'Karaka' is not much. These are
adverse indications denying the birth of brothers.

The Third House.—In Chart No. 62 the third house
is Aries ruled by Mars, Bhratrukaraka. It is not occupied
by any planet but aspected by Jupiter from the eleventh.
Though Jupiter's aspect by itself is good, Jupiter is vitiated
due to contact with Ketu.

The Third Lord.—The lord of the third Mars occupies
the 6th an evil place, where he is not only debilitated but
is combined with the lord of the 6th, *viz.,* waning Moon.

Chart No. 62.—*Born on 24-8-1889 at 5-41 p.m.
(L.T.) Lat. 16° 4' N., Long. 82° 23' E.*

		Venus Rahu	Rahu		Saturn	Jupit. Venus
Lagna		Moon Mars				Sun
	RASI			NAVAMSA		
		Sat. Merc. Sun	Mars			
Jupit. Ketu			Moon	Mercury	Lagna Mandi	Ketu

Balance of Mercury Dasa at birth : Years 16–8–29.

Hence there is considerable affliction to the lord of the third. The only relieving feature is Mars exalted in Navamsa, here again aspected by the Sun. These are decidedly adverse indications.

Lord of Brothers.—Mars, the karaka, is subject to the same afflictions as the lord.

Conclusion.—Though the third house is somewhat favourable, as the lord *cum* the karaka is severely afflicted, the subject has no brothers.

A Practical Experience

The twelve houses or *Dwadasabhavas* in a horoscope comprehend the entire human activities from birth to death. The considerations involved are complex. It is a very difficult task for an astrologer to study carefully all the planetary influences systematically and find out the benefic and malefic elements contributed by the different planets. Moreover the astrologer has to deal with a human being who is not a mere combination of physical substances. Human nature is such an elusive thing that it is hardly capable of being comprehended by the finite mind of man. Anyway astrology gives us principles which enable us to estimate the general worth of an individual and the prosperity and the adversity that will attend him in his life's journey. After having studied the various influences carefully the astrologer must be able to perceive intuitionally the effects and reason cannot enter into the sphere of intuition.

First House.—The first house indicates the body, the health in general, personality and character. The Lagna or ascendant is the actual foundation and on its strong or weak disposition depends the foundation of the horoscope. If the Lagna is powerful, even though other malefic

Chart No. 63.—*Birth details withheld for obvious reasons.*

		Mandi					Sun Venus Sat.
Merc. Rahu		Moon Jupit.	Moon				Mars Ketu
	RASI			NAVAMSA			
Sun		Ketu	Rahu				
Lagna Mars Venus	Saturn			Mercury	Jupiter	Lagna	

Balance of Mercury Dasa at birth : Years 5–1–16.

combinations may be present, the native will have a more or less smooth sailing of his affairs.

In this case the Lagna is Sagittarius and its lord Jupiter gets an innate strength of 9.59 rupas. He is by far the strongest planet in the horoscope and since he is also the Lagnadhipathi, the foundation is quite sound. Lagna is occupied by Mars and Venus and is aspected by Saturn. Thus the determinants of Lagna Bhava are Jupiter, Mars, Venus and Saturn—the chief being Jupiter ; the secondary determinants are Mars and Venus while the tertiary determinant is, of course, Saturn. Therefore these four planets affect the first house indications as also the Moon either as sub-lords or lords. In the Navamsa, Lagna is Virgo and the lord is in the sign of Mars free from affliction. In the Navamsa also Lagna is not subjected to any malefic association or aspect. Thus on the whole both the Lagna and Lagnadhipathi are fairly powerful. I

Rasi Lagnadhipathi is aspected by Mars lord of the 5th
and 12th and Saturn lord of the 2nd and the 3rd. These
aspects act as a slight blemish.

लग्न नवांश पतुल्य तनुस्याद्बलीवंयुत अह्तुल्यतनुवीं ।
चन्द्रसमेन नवांशय वर्गः कादि विलग्न विमक्तभगातः ॥

According to this the native will correspond in his
look to the lord of the rising Navamsa; or his appearance
will correspond to the nature of the strongest planet. His
complexion will partake of the colour of the lord of the
sign occupied by the Moon in the Navamsa. In this case
—as between the strongest planet in the horoscope, *viz.*,
Jupiter and the lord of the Navamsa Lagna (Mercury) the
former is more powerful, the person's nature and appearance correspond to the characteristics of Jupiter. Thus
he will be middle sized with fairly good complexion, and
organs proportionately formed. The disposition of Lagna
lifts him high by his own merits to a position of considerable honour and celebrity. The Lagna gives him the
inclination to taste the good things of life. As Mars has
to do something with the Lagna he is enabled to exercise
authority without harshness and be firm with a pleasantness
of manner.

As the Lagnadhipathi is powerful his health will be
generally good and sound. As Mars is in Lagna with
Venus the constitution will be hot and the tendency later
on in life would be to get piles and other bloody diseases.
The same position of Mars makes him mentally and
morally brave. Other characteristics of the presence of
Mars here are he will be a jolly sort of person, fond of
company, rather passionate, apt to be superficial in thought
and profess knowledge rather than possess it. Venus in
the same place gives him sympathy, agreeable and obliging
manners. Though the situation of Mars in Lagna is quite

favourable in its own way, in this case there is a tendency to suffer from certain physical disabilities. According to the astrological dicta if Mars is in Lagna, the native will be injured by an iron staff and suffers from head and eye diseases. Especially that Mars aspects the Moon, one of the *netrakarakas*, this disposition of Mars should be carefully noted. The native is susceptible to blood-pressure, dizziness of the head, and the like.

General Observations

The dispositions of Lagna, the Sun and the Moon are of paramount importance in assigning the true worth of a horoscope. The Sun rules or represents the Ego, the Moon rules over the mind and the Lagna rules over the body. In fact these three form the tripod of life. In this case the Sun is in Capricorn—a movable and inimical sign which happens to be the 2nd from Lagna. In Navamsa he is in a double-bodied or common sign associated with two malefics. The Sun is fairly powerful having obtained 4.58 rupas as his total shadbala strength. Generally speaking the situation of the Sun makes the emotions active. The Sun gives him a magnetic personality. The vitality will be good. The person carries about him a peculiar charm which makes those that come into contact with him show their respect and regard. He will be kind, loving and warm-hearted. His impulses are of a generous nature as the Sun is aspected by Jupiter. In Navamsa the Sun is with Saturn and Venus but here also he is aspected by Jupiter. This makes his spiritual life but somewhat clouded in material attachments. He is independent and detests being dictated to by others. The situation of the Sun in Navamsa suggests that there will be a distinct conflict between ideals and practices. He will no doubt plan his life's activities keeping in view certain noble ideals. But his environment does not allow him to put into practice what is dear to his heart in the spiritual life. As Jupiter aspects the Sun the soul tries to assert its individuality, but it cannot shake off the shell of attachment. However as age advances he will live up to his ideals. He inherently possesses faith. He is ardent and sincere in his affections. Jupiter's aspect both in Rasi and Navamsa enables him to combine the ideal with real and the practical with the philosophical. As Mars is associated with Venus his personal life will be marked by strong passions.

The Moon's situation in a movable sign makes the mind wavering and somewhat unsteady. Jupiter's association with the Moon partially blemished by Saturn's aspect is of very great importance. This makes him impartial, just, accurate and aiming to be precise; persistent and careful and diligent. The same combination enables him to forget and forgive and vindictiveness does not find a congenial place in his mind. Another characteristic of this combination is that he is more or less self-conscious of what he is. Exalted Saturn aspects the Moon.

Therefore in spite of his good position Saturn makes him sometimes melancholic, doubtful and sceptical but Jupiter restores the equilibrium. He will have a practical conception of things and Jupiter's association with the Moon makes him calm, cool and contemplative of things divine. In the Navamsa again the Moon is in Aquarius aspected by Mars and Jupiter, the former being debilitated. This makes him homely in habits and attached to family. Martian influence enables him to show much positiveness and independence.

It will be seen that both the Sun and the Moon are in variable signs. It is true that the Moon is very well placed and that he is in association with Jupiter. But still in Rasi he is subjected to the aspects of Mars, the Sun and Saturn

—all malefics. This makes him somewhat pessimistic. This does not mean that he lacks self-confidence. He will of course be bold but on account of the presence of Ketu in the 2nd from the Moon and the presence of the Sun in the 2nd from the Lagna he will sometimes become petulant. Again, the Moon's presence suggests that the mind is clear and quick at apprehending things and assimilating new ideas. Dhanus or Sagittarius rising gives an exaggerated faith in human nature. He will be frank, generous, will have more regard for actions than to their results. Dhanus is a common sign and Mars being there aspected by Saturn may give him a somewhat double nature. The sense of justice is keen and harshness to others amounts almost to a personal injury. Summing up the results of the dispositions of Lagna, the Sun and the Moon, we have to observe that the person is sincere, generous and magnanimous, somewhat ambitious, and not fond of show or pomp. The native is sensitive, easily influenced by prevailing circumstances. Emotion plays a large part. Sense of justice, compassion, kindness and deep affection are all features well marked in his nature. Whatever may be general worth of the horoscope, one drawback seems to be that the mind is subject to worry. The power of reason and investigation is strongly marked. Inspirational tendencies are present. He will have much independence of thought which is sometimes affected through deep feelings. The mental and physical abilities are well balanced. He is a self-conscious personality, full of hope, combined with much industry and perseverance. It will be seen that four planets are in Chara Rasis. This bestows an active temperament. Feelings pass quickly into action.

The Second House

The second house represents family, face, right eye, literary gift, self-acquisition, optimism. Of course, wealth

is the important indication of this house.   Money matters
are judged largely, but not exclusively by the 2nd house.
Because while the 2nd indicates wealth the source of earning comes from the 10th and whether one becomes wealthy
or not is judged from the 9th and 11th.   Thus a number
of houses have a bearing on wealth. As usual the 2nd
lord, the karaka and the 2nd house play a large part in
moulding the financial affairs.

In this horoscope the 2nd lord is Saturn and he is
exalted in the 11th.   In the 2nd are placed the Sun as well
as Mercury, lords of the 9th and 10th respectively, and
the whole combination derives the aspect of Jupiter and
the Moon. Jupiter the Dhanakaraka is being aspected by
Saturn lord of the 2nd.   Thus it will be seen that on the
2nd house are brought to bear the concentrated effects of
the influences of exalted Jupiter and Saturn and the lords
of the 10th and 9th.   Jupiter is also lord of Lagna.   Thus
it will be seen that the forces of Lagna, the 2nd, 9th and
10th houses are strongly focussed.   The primary determinant of the 2nd house is of course Saturn while the
subordinate determinants are Jupiter, the Sun, Mercury
and to a certain extent the Moon.   Dhanakaraka in this
case happens to be lord of Lagna which is a force to reckon
with.   Viewed from the Moon the 2nd lord Sun is in the
7th while the 9th lord, *viz*., Jupiter is exalted in Chandra
Lagna. The 2nd from the Moon again receives the aspect
of Mercury and Rahu while Ketu is in the 2nd.   In the
Navamsa the 2nd lord from Lagna is in the 10th (of course
with the 12th lord Sun).   Jupiter's presence in the 2nd is
itself a powerful disposition. From the Moon the 2nd lord
is again Jupiter while Saturn aspects the 2nd.

All these various dispositions are powerful indeed to
give much wealth and financial prosperity.   Saturn is the
most predominant planet to influence the person's financial

affairs. The natural tendency is to gain through the lord of the 2nd. As lord of the 2nd is in the 11th it promises gain through co-operation ; a strong desire to get wealth and possess it is one of the qualities to be found in the person. This desire will be actuated not so much by selfish motives but in order to be in a position to live well and spend well for nobler purposes. Since Saturn is powerful, gain by labour, responsibility, trading in dark or white metals, storage, investments and minerals is also indicated. Saturn has predominantly to do with labour and as he is in the 11th, gain through employing labour on a large scale will be the important source of wealth and gains. Since Jupiter is equally powerful acquisition of wealth through managements, trusts and bankings can also be expected. The Moon's favourable disposition in his own house aspecting the 2nd house signifies earnings from factories and business where a large number of hands are employed. Mercury is no doubt powerful in a way as he is in the 2nd with the Sun, the 9th lord. But as he is also with Rahu in the Rasi much success is not shown in speculation. Some wealth through chance games may be expected by prudent investments. The disposition of the 2nd lord (in the Navamsa) in the 10th is good in its own way: the association with the Sun lord of the 12th is indicative of some sudden financial loss. Financial losses in this case may also happen through the fraudulent conduct of others. Gains from totally unexpected sources are also likely. Investments in coal, shipping and the like would also prove profitable. The 12th lord's association in Amsa denotes waste, sometimes over-liberal tendencies and losses through carelessness, particularly in the major period of Mars. As Mercury is with Rahu without any relieving features some loss is foreseen through bursting of speculative bubbles.

Let us examine some of the more important combinations for wealth. We have already seen that lord of the 2nd and lord of Lagna are both *pre-eminently* powerful. We are specially using the word 'pre-eminently' to stress its importance. This disposition of the lords of Lagna and the 2nd assures financial prosperity throughout life and he will never feel want. Mercury lord of the 7th is no doubt in the bhava but this indicates no material benefits from the wife. One of the powerful Dhanayogas is the presence of lord of Lagna in the 2nd, the 2nd lord in the 11th and the 11th lord in Lagna. In this case this combination is applicable with a slight modification. Lord of Lagna aspects the 2nd, the 2nd lord is in the 11th (exalted) and the 11th lord Venus is in Lagna. This is a powerful combination to which alone should be ascribed the native's high financial status.

Most of his wealth will be due entirely to his own exertions is evident from the fact the planet owning the Rasi occupied by the lord of the Navamsa in which Lagnadhipathi is placed, is exalted or in his own house. Lord of Lagna Jupiter is in Libra Navamsa. Its lord Venus is in Sagittarius and its lord Jupiter is of course exalted and is himself Lagnadhipathi. This combination also gives power to Venus—to be capable of producing results pertaining to finance. From Arudha Lagna Venus is in the 11th house and this must also give rise to much wealth according to the dictum.

लाभे दौल्येन्द्रपूज्यस्य बहुद्रव्यस्यनायकः ।

Venus is in association with Mars and thereby transmits some of his power to Mars. Another important combination for wealth is, Jupiter must reside in the second or own the 2nd, or aspect the lord. In Navamsa the second house is occupied by Jupiter and the 2nd lord from the Moon is Jupiter. These have also added considerably to the financial worth.

One of the most important dispositions is the exchange or parivarthana in its subtle aspect between Jupiter and Saturn, the two important planets in this horoscope. It will be seen that Jupiter is in the constellation of Pushyami ruled by Saturn while Saturn is posited in Visakha the constellation ruled by Jupiter. This interchange of constellations between 1st and 2nd lords is of unique importance and this suggests the person having earnings without much effort.

Summing up the above, we have to observe that the house of wealth is very well disposed. Saturn's presence in the 11th is highly conducive for a steady flow of fortune. Mars Dasa would be highly prosperous so far as financial prosperity is concerned.

Sarwarthachinthamani says that if lord of Lagna is more powerful than any other planet and joins Jupiter he will have much self-acquired wealth. According to *Jathakathathwa*, acquisition of treasure is likely if the 11th lord is in the 1st, the 1st lord is in the 2nd and the 2nd lord is in the 11th. This combination is practically applicable here and therefore the native is likely to land some treasure-trove also.

The native should be careful about his eyes. The Moon is no doubt in his own place with exalted Jupiter and the Sun is no doubt aspected by the same Jupiter. But still according to the dictum "that if the Moon and Jupiter are conjoined in the 6th, 8th or 12th, one becomes blind through excess of seminal effusion", it is likely that the eye-sight might suffer as age advances.

The Third House

The third rules brothers and sisters, intelligence, cousins and other immediate relations.

The third house is Aquarius, a fixed sign, occupied by Mercury (lord of the 7th and 10th) and Rahu and aspected by no planets. According to bhava, Mercury comes to the 2nd bhava though the results have to be based on the Rasi position also to an appreciable extent. Lord of the 3rd Saturn is in the 11th exalted and of course subject to no aspects. Mars the karaka for brothers is in Lagna aspected by lord of brothers and in association with the lord of the house of elder brother.

If the lord of Lagna and lord of wealth are connected in anyway with lord of house of brothers, then the relations between brothers will be cordial and there will be mutual benefits accruing. In other words, the financial disposition of the native improves on account of the brothers. From the Moon lord of the 3rd Mercury is in the 8th—while in the Navamsa, the 3rd lord is Mars and he is in the 11th from Lagna. Lagna, the karaka for brothers and lord of the 3rd are all connected with each other in some way or the other. All these dispositions indicate that the relations between the native and the brothers will be generally cordial and there will be mutual benefits accruing. His own financial disposition improves on account of brothers. But on account of the 3rd lord's disposition from the Moon, some distrust or misunderstanding is possible especially in Mercury's sub-period within the Dasa of Rahu. The misunderstandings will be largely due to strings being pulled by other members of the family. Lord of Lagna being exalted the native will be noble and generous in his disposition towards them but they will try to impute motives to him and take advantage of his kindness. It will be seen that Rahu is in the 3rd. This is good so far as it goes. This gives the native courage and boldness to meet awkward situations and overcome opposition. This will also give him at times melancholia and morbid tendencies in regard to dealings with relatives. The position of Rahu shows also a religious and philosophical mind, kind and sympathetic mentality. On account of the favourable disposition of Mars, the brothers will generally be well placed in life. The third being a fixed sign gives a fixed and determined attitude : Rahu in this particular position widens the mental vision add broadens the intellectual view of life. It also raises the mind to higher thought and prepares the way for altruistic ideals and mental reforms. It tends to make one a distinct and unique character especially in mental expression. Rahu also gives sudden and unexpected journeys and gains through such travels. In short, there will be cordiality with brothers, generally speaking, and from a business point, gain is indicated through association with brothers.

7. Concerning the Fourth House

In previous chapters I have dealt rather exhaustively with the first three of the twelve houses or bhavas constituting a horoscope. In astrology, we are used to regarding each house or bhava as representing or signifying certain definite functions or events. Often there is a certain jumbling of the events assigned to a house that a student of astrology gets somewhat bewildered at the apparent inconsistency.

The fourth has reference to mother, immovable property, education, vehicles and general happiness. It follows as a matter of course that an affliction to the fourth house may result in the shape of depriving the person of peace of mind, causing misfortune to his mother, troubles in regard to property affairs and so on. But in reality, a person may be educated but may also lose his mother early. He may command good immovable properties but may not be happy. Most of us seek to use astrology from a practical point of view. I have endeavoured to deal with each signification of a bhava separately. The greatest difficulty in astrology is to differentiate the different events comprehended by a bhava. And the procedure adopted by me is designed to obviate this difficulty to some extent.

Primary Considerations

Before analysing the fourth bhava, one has to carefully study the general strength of (a) the bhava, (b) the karaka, and (c) its lord and the occupants. Of the various yogas present in the horoscope, those that have a bearing on the fourth house should be carefully noted.

We shall first consider the general combinations and then the effects of planets severally. The fourth, like the tenth, is a very important house and is in fact the pivot around which revolve some of the special events affecting the individual's life.

Results of the Lord of the Fourth House Occupying Different Houses

First House. – The person becomes highly learned, but will be afraid to speak in public assemblies. He is likely to lose inherited wealth. According as the fourth lord posited in Lagna is strong, middling or weak, the native will have been born in a rich, mediocre or poor family.

Second House. —He will be highly fortunate. courageous and happy. He will have a sarcastic nature. He will inherit property from maternal grandfather.

Third House. —The person will be sickly, generous, a man of character, and will acquire wealth by self-effort. He will suffer from the machinations of step-brothers and step-mother.

Fourth House. —Religiously inclined, will have respect for traditions. He will be rich, respected, happy and sensual.

Fifth House. – Loved and respected by others, devotee of Vishnu, becomes rich by self-effort. Mother comes from a respectable family. The native will acquire vehicles.

Sixth House. —Short-tempered and mean, he will have dissimulating habits, evil thoughts and intentions. He will always be roaming about.

Seventh House.—Generally happy; will command houses and lands; will eke out livelihood in distant places or near his birthplace according as the seventh happens to be a movable or fixed sign.

Eighth House.—The person becomes miserable. Father dies early. He will be either impotent or loose in sex-life. He is also likely to lose landed properties or face litigation.

Ninth House.—Generally a fortunate combination favouring happiness in regard to father and properties.

Tenth House.—Will have political success. He will be an expert chemist. He will vanquish his enemies and make his personality felt by the world. Loss of reputation is posible if the 4th lord is afflicted.

Eleventh House.— Self-made, generous, sickly, mother fortunate, but may have a step-mother also. Favours success in selling and buying cattle and lands.

Twelfth House—Deprived of happiness and properties. Early death to mother, bad finances and generally a miserable existence.

It must be clearly noted that these combinations are very general and they should not be applied verbatim. The good and bad nature of results ascribed to the fourth lord occupying a certain house becomes augmented or minimised according to the strength or weakness of the fourth lord. The great Satyacharya, for instance, says that when the fourth lord, subjected to subha vargas or favourable aspects, is in the third, one acquires very little of immovable property and that such a fourth lord is also capable of depriving the person of his meagre possessions, besides involving him in trouble on account of his step-mother and step-brothers. If the fourth lord is moderately afflicted, the evil nature is somewhat tempered. If the

11

fourth lord is strongly afflicted, there will be an intensification of the evil results ascribed.

In judging any bhava, one's interpretation must be intelligent and skilled and not literal.

Important Combinations

I shall give below some important combinations pertaining to the fourth house:

If the lord of the fourth house occupies the sixth, eighth and twefth and has no beneficial aspect, there will be early death of the mother. The lord of the fourth house in Lagna and Venus in the fourth, strongly disposed, will confer vehicles, jewels and wealth. If the lord of the fourth is in a dusthana or if the fourth house is occupied by Mars or Saturn, the person will lose his property and wealth. If Jupiter is in the fourth and the fourth lord joins good planets, the person will have good friends. One associates with bad people if the fourth or the fourth lord is subjected to Papakarthari Yoga. Lords of the second, fourth and twelfth in kendras and thrikonas ensure smoothness in affairs pertaining to property and houses. The fourth lord in Lagna or in the seventh gives one a house without any difficulty. Lord of the fourth in the eighth, afflicted or debilitated, deprives the person of his lands and houses. If there is Parivarthana (interchange) between the lords of the fourth and tenth, one gets lands. If the lords causing Parivarthana are extremely strong, and attain Gopuramsa, the person may even become a ruler. Parivarthana Yoga between the fourth and sixth lords favours getting lands from enemies, by right. Jupiter weak and evil planets in the fourth render one unhappy with wealth. The person loses lands by royal or Government orders if the lord of the fourth is neecha with Sun. One becomes a great sinner if many evil planets are in the fourth and the fourth lord is in an enemy's house. If the fourth lord is weak, debilitated and joined by evil planets and Lagna is in a watery sign, the person falls in water. The person will be drowned if the weak lord of the Lagna is in the fourth, which should be a watery sign. The Sun and Mars in the fourth give wounds from stones. The Moon in the fourth joined or aspected by evil planets kills the mother early. The person will be reserved if the fourth is occupied by evil planets, or if Mars, Saturn or Rahu is in the fourth without good associations. The native's heart will be clean if Jupiter is in or aspects the fourth. He will be a hypocrite, sweet in words but dangerous at heart if Rahu, joined or aspected by evil planets, is in the fourth. He wins the affection of mother if lord of Lagna and the fourth are friendly, and are otherwise beneficially disposed. There will be enmity with mother if the fourth lord is in the eighth from Lagna or from lord of Lagna. If the strong lords of the fourth and ninth aspected by Jupiter are disposed in kendras (angles) or konas (trines), there will be favours from royalty. One gets commission in the army if the fourth lord is with Mars in favourable disposition.

Planets in the Fourth House

The Sun.—This combination is said to make one generally unhappy and mentally worried. He will be roaming about. The position promises some inheritance. He will have interest in occult and philosophical studies. In the political field success is difficult. Obstacles in life are shown if Saturn or Mars aspects the Sun.

The Moon.—Possesses house; derives happiness from relatives; will be cheerful and contented; becomes important as a leader or ruler; proud and somewhat quarrel-

some. The position indicates early separation from the
mother if the Moon is afflicted; will be fond of sensual
pleasures, unless aspected by Jupiter.

Mars.—This is generally a bad combination. The
person will be deprived of happiness from mother, relations and friends, but will have success in the political
line. There will be quarrels with mother and domestic
affairs go awry. If Mars joins Rahu or Ketu, the man
will have a tendency for suicide. The person will own
houses but will not be happy on that account.

Mercury.—Shines well as an educationist or diplomat.
He will boldly criticise the Government. He will be held
in great esteem. Father will be a self-made man. He
will command a good conveyance. He will have taste for
music and other fine arts and will frequently travel to far
off countries. He will be witty in speech.

Jupiter.—Philosophically inclined, learned, happy,
possesses the favour of the ruling class; a terror to his
enemies; religiously inclined, respected and fortunate;
peaceful domestic environments; great spiritual advancement.

Venus.—Well versed in music, polished manners, deep
attachment to mother, many friends, conveyances and
houses; religious by inclined; successful achievement of
desires. This is a favourable yoga for affairs of a domestic
nature, concord and happiness.

Saturn.—Sickly during early years; deprived of
mother and unhappy; suffers from windy and phlegmatic
complaints; lethargic temperament; will not inherit any
property; will have troubles from houses and vehicles;
disliked by relatives; desire to live a very secluded life;
unfavourable for domestic or family affairs, unless
beneficially aspected or associated.

Rahu.—Foolish in behaviour; few friends; will be subjected to fraud ; or guilty of fraudulent action.

Ketu.—Will be deprived of mother, properties and happiness; lives in a foreign place. There will be exceptional experiences at the end of life. There will be reversals and sudden changes.

It will be seen that the nature of results supposed to be given by the Sun and other planets remaining in the fourth house gets modified by the aspects and conjunctions of other planets. If the Sun is strengthened, there will be financial benefits by inheritance; if afflicted, there will be trouble through political sources. If the Moon is fortified, that is well aspected or conjoined, the person will have mental peace. If afflicted, adverse changes are denoted. If the afflicted planet is Saturn, the mother dies early. If Mars is the afflicted planet, there will be loss through theft, deception and even litigation. Affliction of Mars always denotes some tragic developments in the personal life, quarrels, strife and misunderstandings. If Mars is involved in benefic association or aspect, there will be a certain amount of tempering of the evil. Mercury afflicted denotes mental distress, frauds and misery. Well disposed, it is a good position for intellectual and literary attainments. Jupiter afflicted causes hardships and obstacles. Well fortified it is a sure indication of prosperity in regard to all the events of the fourth house. The person will have a peaceful home-life. Venus in affliction denotes looseness in morals and abuse of artistic talents. Venus well fortified is a great asset for the horoscope. It indicates a bright career as an artist. Saturn's position in the fourth, unless he is Lagnadhipathi, is not favoured. It deprives the man of peace of mind and the affection of the mother. The person likes a secluded life. An affliction

by Mars indicates a sudden downfall. It is also a combination for insanity. Rahu–Mars or Ketu–Mars affliction
shows tragedy or violence. Rahu–Saturn or Ketu–Saturn
affliction may denote mental disorder, hysteria and even
insanity. In all these cases, a careful weighing of the *pros*
and *cons* of the affliction or fortification is absolutely
necessary. No slip-shod interpretation should be made
and a premature conclusion arrived at.

Time of Fructification of the Results of the Fourth House

Each bhava must be studied not in an isolated manner
but as having a bearing on every other part of the horoscope. This collective approach is absolutely necessary
if we have to understand the true significance of a bhava.

The factors governing the fourth house are (a) the
lord, (b) planet or planets aspecting the fourth house,
(c) planet or planets posited in the fourth, (d) planets
aspecting the lord of the fourth, (e) planet or planets in
association with the lord of the fourth, (f) the lord of the
fourth from the Moon, and (g) the karaka of the fourth
bhava.

The factors suggested above may influence the fourth
house, that is give rise to the results of the fourth house,
(a) as lords of Dasas (periods), as lords of Bhuktis (sub-
periods), or as lords of the still minor divisions of the
Dasa scheme. It must be noted that the sub-periods of
the planets capable of influencing the fourth, in the major
periods of those capable of influencing the fourth, produce
results pertaining to the fourth house *par excellence*. (2)
The sub-periods of planets, associated with the fourth
house in the major periods of planets, not associated with
the fourth house, will give rise to results pertaining to the
fourth house only to a limited extent. Similarly, the sub-
periods whose lords have nothing to do with the fourth

house, in the major periods whose lords are associated
with the fourth, will produce effects pertaining to the
fourth house only to a limited or even nominal extent.
It must be noted that the term "association or associated"
used in this context connotes aspect as well as
conjunction.

Where a lord is involved in a Raja yoga or Arishta
yoga, the lord is capable of producing in his Dasa or
Bhukti the Raja yoga or Arishta yoga results, so far as
they relate to the fourth house. Let us assume that a
Rajabhanga Neecha Yoga is caused by the lord of the
fourth. During his Dasa or Bhukti, he can bring about
the destruction of the Raja yoga so far as the fourth
house indications go. If a man owns houses and cars,
he may lose them. If he has properties, they may be
auctioned.

The Nature of Results

The general principles enunciated in regard to the
three Bhavas dealt with in the previous chapters hold good
for the fourth house also. In general, the following
results, subject of course to the peculiarity of the individual horoscope concerned, may be anticipated in the
Dasas and Bhuktis of the planets capable of influencing
the fourth house in the various capacities mentioned on
page 14.

The fourth lord strongly placed in a kendra or
thrikona : Acquisition of knowledge, lands, houses and
happiness. The native will take to agriculture, dig wells
and lay out fine gardens. If the fourth lord joins the fifth
lord in the fifth or there is Parivarthana between the
fourth and fifth lords, the native gets political fame. He
will enter the Parliament, and get the post of a speaker ;
earns plenty of money and inherits properties. In the sub-

period of the fourth lord, there will be birth of a son.
When both the karaka and the lord are strong, he will
definitely get the grace of the rulers. When the fourth
lord is in the sixth, eighth or twelfth, the native will
experience contrary results in the sub-period of the fourth
lord. If the Lagnadhipati is afflicted, there will be an
endless source of trouble from the authorities. He will
lose his property and become a victim of the ruler's wrath.
Where both the fourth and fifth lords are weak, the results
described above will happen nominally.

When the fourth lord is in the sixth with the sixth lord
and the karaka is strongly disposed, the person will acquire
lands during the Dasa of the fourth lord. He will have
happiness from mother, acquisition of knowledge. When
the fourth lord joins the seventh lord in the seventh, the
native will reside for some time in a foreign place and
acquire lands and wealth. If the fourth lord occupies a
Navamsa which is the sixth, eighth or twelfth from the
Navamsa held by the seventh lord, there is likelihood of
death also. The person will definitely lose his property,
vehicles and cattle or will involve himself in litigation in
the Dasa of the fourth lord, if the fourth lord is in the
eighth with the eighth lord. The mother will fall ill or die.
There will be an end to education. The evil gets mitigated
if in Navamsa, the fourth lord occupies the sixth, eighth
or twelfth from the eighth lord.

When the fourth lord is in the ninth with the ninth
lord and the karaka is equally well disposed, the person
gets sudden fortune and wealth in the Dasa of the fourth
lord. In the Navamsa, if the fourth lord is in the sixth,
eighth or twelfth from the ninth lord, contrary results
will happen. If the fourth lord is in the tenth with the
tenth lord and is otherwise strong, the person becomes a

Minister or a high placed Government servant. If Mercury happens to be lord of the fourth or tenth, there will be access to wealth through trade and business channels. One will earn in trade and commerce if the fourth lord is in the eleventh with the eleventh lord. If the fourth lord occupies the sixth, eighth or twelfth (in Navamsa) from the position of the eleventh lord, there will be losses. The earnings or losses will be from sources appropriate to the natures of the planets concerned. If the fourth lord is in the twelfth with the twefth lord, the person will have mental worry, loss of cattle, misfortunes to mother and involvement in troubles. The evils will be somewhat tempered if the fourth lord is more powerful than the twelfth lord.

Health, spiritual progress, happiness from father, new friendships, agreeable food are the results conferred in the Dasa of the fourth lord in association with Lagnadhipati or Navamsa Lagnadhipati.

As we have seen above the fourth has reference to mother, happiness, acquisition of learning and vehicles and immovable properties. I propose to deal with each of these items separately for purposes of studying example horoscopes.

Vaidyanatha Deekshitar wants us to look to the fourth house and Jupiter for judging happiness; the Moon and the fourth for mother; for vehicles and ornaments Venus and the fourth bhava. By studying a number of illustrations, it would be possible for any student of astrology to formulate for himself astrological principles governing the analysis of the fourth bhava in all its details.

Mother

Mother's long life should be estimated by the strength of the fourth house and the fact of the Moon occupying a

benefic sign in a kendra and aspected by benefic planet.
It is also possible to anticipate the longevity of the mother
by considering the fourth house or Matrukaraka as the
ascendant of the mother and studying the strength or
otherwise of the eighth house therefrom. Generally when
the lord of the fourth is in the sixth or twelfth, weak, and
the Lagna is joined by a malefic, there will be early loss
of mother. The following combinations may also be
noted :—

(i) Waning Moon in association with a malefic in
the sixth or eighth house.

(ii) Saturn in the fourth with the Moon.

The Fourth House.—The fourth has two planets,
Saturn and the Moon in Chart No. 64. Saturn's presence
in the fourth is good as lord of Lagna and bad as a
natural malefic. The affliction is heavy because of association with the Moon lord of the sixth. The fourth is

Chart No. 64.—*Born on 8-8-1912 A.D. at 7-35 p.m.*
(I.S.T.) (Lat. 13° N., Long. 5h. 10m. 20s. E.)

Rahu		Moon Saturn		Saturn	Venus
Lagna		Sun	Sun Rahu	NAVAMSA	
	RASI	Mars Merc. Venus	Lagna		Merc. Moon Ketu
	Jupiter	Ketu		Jupiter	Mars

Balance of Mars Dasa at birth :   Years 6–1–6.

aspected by Jupiter. The aspect is good because Jupiter is a natural benefic and bad as Jupiter is a malefic for Aquarius Lagna. The fourth house is fairly strong.

Matrukaraka (Lord of Mother).—The Moon owns the 6th and hence afflicted. Matrukaraka's association with Saturn here gives rise to considerable affliction though there is a little relief due to Jupiter's aspect. Above all, the karaka for the mother in the appropriate bhava is not a happy combination.

The Fourth Lord.—The lord of the fourth Venus is in the 4th from the bhava in association with two malefics Mars and Mercury and hemmed in between the Sun and Ketu. In the Navamsa also the fourth lord Venus is considerably afflicted on account of the aspect of Mars.

Considered from the Moon.—The fourth lord Sun is in the twelfth from the fourth subjected to the aspects of Saturn and Jupiter, the latter being evil by virtue of the eighth and eleventh lordship from Chandra Lagna. The fourth is hemmed in between malefics and joined by three planets.

Summing up, the fourth house as such is not weak but Matrukaraka is definitely afflicted indicating early death to mother.

The following planets can give the results of the fourth house with special reference to mother :—

1. Moon—as Matrukaraka.
2. Saturn—as an associate of Matrukaraka.
3. Jupiter—as aspecting Matrukaraka.
4. Venus—as lord of fourth house.
5. Mars and Mercury—as associating with fourth lord.

In Chart No. 64 all the above planets can influence the fourth house either in their Dasas or in their Bhuktis. Since the longevity of the person is about 75 years, Mars,

Jupiter, Saturn and Mercury can influence—both as mjaor
and sub-lords while the Moon and Venus can give the
effects of the fourth house only as sub-lords. Theoreti-
cally speaking, the mother could enjoy Rajayoga results
when the native undergoes Saturn Dasa, as Saturn would
be a yogakaraka for the fourth bhava. Equally beneficial
results could be anticipated for the mother when the
native enjoys Mercury Dasa. But because there are no
combinations for the long life of the mother, Saturn and
Mercury influencing the fourth bhava as major lords are
ruled out. Nor could they confer the beneficial results on
the mother as sub-lords. Mars, it will be seen, is a maraka
from Matrukaraka and joins Mercury who happens to be
a maraka for the sign held by Matrukaraka. Consequently
death of the mother can be expected. Saturn joining Matrukaraka can bring about the destruction of the mother.
Moreover, the native at birth was passing through *sade-*

Chart No. 65.—*Born on 16-11-1914 at 5 p.m. (Lat.
27° 55' N., Long. 68° 45' E.)*

Lagna Mandi		Sat.		Mandi	
Rahu			Moon Merc.		Ketu Sun
	RASI			**NAVAMSA**	
Jupit.		Ketu	Sat. Rahu		Lagna Jupit.
	Sun Mars Venus	Moon Mercury	Venus		Mars

Balance of Rahu Dasa at birth :   Years 6-7-28.

sathi. All these accelerated the death of the mother which took place in Mars Dasa, Saturn Bhukti.

The Fourth House.—In Chart No. 65 the fourth is Cancer a movable sign and is devoid of any benefic or malefic associations. The fourth is aspected by debilitated Jupiter.

Fourth Lord.—The fourth lord Moon is in the seventh with Mercury lord of the third and sixth and hence blemished.

Matrukaraka.—The fourth lord is also Matrukaraka in this horoscope. The blemish attached to the fourth lord applies to Matrukaraka.

Rahu is in the fifth from Matrukaraka Moon. Rahu being a shadowy planet should give the results of Mars whose star he occupies, Mars in turn not only owns the second and seventh maraka but is actually situated in the second from Matrukaraka in association with the Sun lord of the second from Matrusthana and Venus lord of the eighth from Matrukaraka. Venus owns the eighth from Matrukaraka and occupies the second. Hence mother's death took place in Rahu Dasa, Venus Bhukti, Venus Antara.

Conclusion.—The fourth house is moderately strong, but the lord and the karaka are considerably afflicted. Hence the native lost his mother very early.

Fourth Bhava.—In Chart No. 66 the fourth is Virgo a double-bodied sign. It is occupied by the Moon, lord of the second and Saturn lord of the eighth and ninth. It is hemmed in on either side by malefics. From Chandra Lagna, the fourth lord Jupiter is in the eighth with Rahu. The fourth house is moderately strong.

Fourth Lord.—Fourth lord Mercury is in the twelfth from the fourth in association with the Sun. Mercury is further aspected by exalted Mars lord of the sixth and

Chart No. 66 —*Born on 25/26–8–1892 at 2–30 a.m. (L.M.T.) (Lat. 12° 52' N., Long. 74° 54' E.)*

	Rahu Jupiter		Lagna Venus	Sat.	Ketu		Lagna Jupiter	Mars Venus
			Mandi					Sun Moon Merc.
	RASI					NAVAMSA		
Mars			Sun Merc.					Mandi
		Ketu	Moon Sat.				Rahu	

Balance of the Moon Dasa at birth : Years 1–5–27.

eleventh and Jupiter lord of the seventh and tenth. The fourth lord is therefore rendered weak.

Matrukaraka.—The Moon is in Matrubhava (4th house). This is definitely injurious to the mother. He has joined Saturn, and is subjected to Papakarthari Yoga.

Conclusion.—Combinations for mother's longevity are not good. Rahu occupies eighth from Matrukaraka and has joined Jupiter as maraka from Matrukaraka. Consequently the mother died in Rahu Dasa Jupiter Bhukti.

It will be seen that Chart Nos. 64 and 66 have both Saturn and the Moon in the fourth. In Chart No. 64 mother died in Mars Dasa Saturn Bhukti, in the second year of the native whereas in Chart No 66 mother lived up to the 13th year of the person. In view of the affliction of the Moon to the same if not to a greater extent as in Chart No. 64 it is reasonable to expect the death of the mother in Moon Dasa itself. But because the Moon in this case is in his own constellation, he could not cause the death of the mother in his own Dasa (period). In Chart No. 64 on the other hand the Moon is in the constellation of Mars, a maraka or death-producing planet (from Matrukraka and Matrubhava) and the mother died in the Dasa of Mars. According to Satyacharya, the fact of a planet being situated in a particular constellation is of paramount importance especially in the matter of predicting significant events.

Chart No. 67.—*Born on 19-2-1900 at 10–24 a.m. (L.M.T.) (Lat. 18° 17′ N., Long. 83° 57′ E.)*

Venus	Lagna	Ketu	Mandi	Merc.			Mandi
Sun Mars Merc.	RASI			Rahu	NAVAMSA		Sat.
							Ketu
Sat.	Jupiter Rahu		Moon	Sun Jupit.	Venus	Lagna Mars	Moon

Balance of Mars Dasa at birth : Years 3–9–8.

The Fourth House.—The fourth house is Cancer a movable sign. It is aspected by Jupiter lord of the ninth and twelfth. The fourth house is not occupied by any planet. From Chandra Lagna, the fourth is occupied by Saturn. In Navamsa, the fourth is aspected by Saturn and Mars. The fourth house is not strongly disposed.

The Fourth Lord.—The fourth lord Moon is in the sixth. He is aspected by Venus (lord of the second and seventh), Mars and Saturn, two first-rate malefics. The fourth lord from Chandra Lagna is in the twelfth from the fourth. In the Navamsa, the Moon is subjected to Papakarthari Yoga and in the Rasi he is aspected by Saturn and Mars. The fourth lord is on the whole weak.

Matrukaraka.—The fourth lord happens to be Matrukaraka also. Hence Matrukaraka has all the weakness of the lord.

Conclusion..—The karaka and the lord being very weak, the mother's longevity is poor. Rahu is in the third from Matrukaraka and has joined Jupiter a maraka from Matrukaraka. Consequently, the mother's death took place in Jupiter Bhukti Rahu Dasa.

Chart No. 68.—*Born on 13–10–1896 at 7–56 a.m. (L.M.T.) (Lat. 8° 53' N., Long. 76° 39' E.)*

		Mars	Mandi	Ketu	Venus	Sat. Lagna
Rahu						Merc. Jupit.
	RASI			**NAVAMSA**		
Mandi		Jupit. Ketu				
Moon	Lagna Saturn Venus	Sun Merc.		Mars	Moon Rahu	Sun

Balance of Venus Dasa at birth : Years 5–2–12.

The Fourth House.—The fourth house is Capricorn a malefic sign free from occupation. The fourth is however aspected by Mars.

Fourth Lord.— The fourth lord Saturn is exalted in Lagna. He is in association with Venus lord of Lagna and is otherwise free from affliction.

Matrukaraka.—The Moon is in the third, a benefic sign, unassociated but aspected by Jupiter lord of the third. This benefic disposition is more than counter-balanced by the combined aspect of two first-rate malefics, *viz.,* Saturn and Mars. In the Navamsa again, the Moon is associated with Rahu and subjected to Papakarthari Yoga. Moreover, Matrukaraka is in a place which happens to be the 12th from Matrusthana. Consequently Matru-karaka is considerably afflicted.

Conclusion.—The aspect of Saturn, as lord of the fourth, on Matrukaraka Moon could have been construed as beneficial but for the fact Saturn happens to be a natural malefic. The fourth is moderately strong. Matrukaraka is feebly strong. The fourth house is considerably afflicted.

Chart No. 69.—*Born on 10-2-1909 at 11-33 a.m. (I.S.T.) (Lat. 12° 20' N., Long. 76° 38' E.)*

Sat.	Lagna		Rahu	Mars	Venus Ketu	
Merc.		RASI			NAVAMSA	Moon
Sun Venus			Jupit.	Mandi		
Ketu	Mandi Mars		Moon		Saturn	Lagna Mercury Jupiter Rahu	Sun

Balance of Moon Dasa at birth : Years 0–1–11.

12

Consequently the person lost his mother in his 16th year in Moon Dasa Saturn Bhukti.

Fourth House.—In Chart No. 69 the fourth house is Cancer a benefic sign. It is unoccupied, but aspected by malefic Sun lord of the 5th and a benefic Venus. In the Navamsa the fourth is aspected by Saturn, lord of the fourth. The fourth house is therefore moderately strong.

Fourth Lord.—The fourth lord Moon is in the 6th in a benefic sign but is aspected by Saturn. Hence blemished.

Matrukaraka.—Since the fourth lord is also Matrukaraka, the blemish attached to the fourth lord is equally applicable to the Matrukaraka.

Conclusion.—The fourth house is moderately strong. But the lord *cum* karaka is considerably afflicted The mother died at the age of 9 in Rahu Dasa Rahu Bhukti. Mark the disposition of Rahu in the twelfth or house of loss from Matrusthana.

Chart No. 70.—*Born on 25-9-1898 at 7-30 a.m. (L.M.T.) (Lat. 23° 2′ N., Long. 72° 19′ E.)*

	Lagna	Mandi	Mars Ketu		Ketu Sun Mars	Moon	Venus
		RASI				NAVAMSA	
Moon			Merc.				Lagna Jupit. Mandi
Rahu	Saturn	Venus	Sun Jupit.		Mercury Saturn	Rahu	

Balance of Moon Dasa at birth : Years 6–7–2.

Fourth House.—In Chart No. 70 the fourth house Cancer is unoccupied by any planet, good or bad. It is aspected by the fourth lord Moon. This is good so far as general indications of the fourth house are concerned. In the Navamsa, the fourth house is considerably afflicted by the presence of Saturn and aspect of Mars.

Fourth Lord.—The fourth lord Moon is in Capricorn a malefic sign, aspected powerfully by Saturn and Mars—two first-rate malefics. Jupiter's aspect is a relieving feature.

Matrukaraka.—As the Moon Matrukaraka himself happens to be the fourth lord, he is subject to all the afflictions of the fourth lord.

Conclusion.—The fourth house is moderately strong. The fourth lord and Matrukaraka are considerably afflicted. The mother died in the 18th year in Moon Dasa Sun Bhukti. Mark that Sun the sub-lord owns the 2nd from Matrusthana and occupies the 3rd.

Chart No. 71.—*Born on 5-7-1886 at 10-32 p.m. (L.M.T.) (Lat. 23° 12' N., Long. 87° 56' E.)*

		Venus	Sun Sat.	Jupit. Ketu	Sun Mars Saturn	Venus	Lagna Mandi
Lagna Ketu			Merc.				
	RASI				NAVAMSA		Moon
Mandi			Moon Rahu				
			Mars Jupit.		Mercury		Rahu

Balance of Venus Dasa at birth : Years 17–8–3.

The Fourth House.—In Chart No. 71 the fourth is Taurus, a benefic sign. It is occupied by its own lord Venus and further aspected by benefic Jupiter. In the Navamsa the fourth is occupied by Rahu but aspected by Jupiter. The fourth house is therefore fairly strong.

The Fourth Lord.—As the fourth lord is in the 4th, he is subject to all the benefic influences of the fourth.

Matrukaraka.—The Moon is in Leo in conjunction with Rahu. The Moon is further aspected by Saturn and hence considerably afflicted.

Conclusion.—The mother lived till the 36th year of the native on account of the general strength of the fourth house and fourth lord. The Matrukaraka Moon, who is the primary indicator of the mother, is considerably afflicted. Mother's death took place in Mars Dasa, Saturn Bhukti. Mark that Mars happens to be a maraka from the 4th house and occupies a maraka place from the Moon,

Chart No. 72.—*Born on 10-4-1910 at 8-38 p.m. (I.S.T.) (Lat. 16° 20' N., Long. 80° 15' E.)*

Sun	Moon Saturn Mercury	Mars Rahu		Sun Rahu		Mercury Saturn	Moon Jupit.
Venus	RASI			Mandi	NAVAMSA		Lagna
				Venus			Mars
	Lagna Ketu Mandi	Jupit.					Ketu

Balance of Ketu Dasa at birth : Years 2-1-25.

and Saturn occupies a maraka place from the fourth house.

The Fourth House.—In Chart No. 72 the fourth is Aquarius, a malefic sign. It is occupied by natural benefic Venus and aspected by no planet. The fourth is not blemished.

The Fourth Lord.—Saturn is the fourth lord. He is neecha in the 6th and is associated with two malefics Moon and Mercury and subjected to a powerful Papakarthari Yoga.

Matrukaraka.—Since Matrukaraka Moon is in the same sign as Saturn, he (Moon) is subject to all the afflictions as Saturn. In addition, the Moon is with a malefic Saturn.

Conclusion.—The fourth house is unblemished. The fourth lord and Matrukaraka are both considerably afflicted with the result the mother died when the native was aged 3 in Venus Dasa Venus Bhukti. Venus happens to be a maraka for the sign containing the Matrukaraka and the 4th lord.

Chart No. 73.—*Born on 5-1-1891 at 12-30 p.m. (L.M.T.) (Lat. 18° 54' N., Long. 72° 49' E.)*

	Lagna	Rahu	Mandi	Merc.		Mars	Lagna
Mars				Moon			Rahu
	RASI		———		NAVAMSA		
Merc. Jupit.			Sat.	Ketu			Jupit.
Sun	Ketu Venus	Moon			Saturn Mandi Sun Venus		

Balance of Rahu Dasa at birth : Years 6–0–27.

The Fourth House.—In Chart No. 73, Cancer the fourth house is not occupied by any planet, good or bad. On the other hand, it is aspected by debilitated Jupiter and Mercury. In the Navamsa also, the fourth is aspected by Mercury who has obtained neechabhanga. Consequently the fourth house is fairly powerful.

The Fourth Lord.—The Moon, lord of the fourth, is Matrukaraka also. He is in Libra, a benefic sign but aspected powerfully by Saturn.

Conclusion.—The fourth house is not much afflicted, but the lord and karaka are moderately blemished. The native lost his mother in Saturn Dasa Venus Bhukti. Saturn is in a maraka from the fourth and Venus is in a maraka from the Moon.

Chart No. 74.—*Born on 21–7–1900 at 10–38 a.m. (L.M.T.) (Lat. 23° 11' N., Long. 79° 53' E.)*

Lagna	Mandi	Ketu Mars Moon	Venus		Moon Venus	Mandi		Ketu Sat.
			Sun Merc.		Merc.			
	RASI				NAVAMSA			Mars
					Lagna			
Sat.	Jupiter Rahu				Rahu		Jupiter	Sun

Balance of the Sun Dasa at birth : Year 0–4–2.

The Fourth House.—The fourth house is Gemini a benefic sign. It is occupied by Venus, who though lord of the 3rd and 8th is a natural benefic. The fourth is further aspected by Saturn and is subjected to Papakarthari Yoga.

The Fourth Lord.—Mercury who owns the fourth is in the fifth in association with the Sun and aspected by Jupiter. He is, if at all, feebly blemished.

Matrukaraka.—The Moon is exalted but in association with Ketu and Mars. This is counterbalanced by Jupiter's aspect. In the Navamsa, the Moon is in a benefic sign in association with exalted Venus.

Conclusion.— All the three elements are feebly blemished. The native's mother died in 1946 when he was aged 46.

Chart No. 75.—*Born on 17-7-1895 at 12-30 p.m. (L.M.T.) (Lat. 11° 0' N., Long. 78° 40' E.)*

		Merc. Jupit.		Mars	Rahu	Jupit.
Rahu		Sun	Merc.			
	RASI			**NAVAMSA**		Sun Lagna
		Mars Ketu Venus				Venus Mandi
	Saturn	Mandi Lagna	Moon Sat.	Ketu		

Balance of Sun Dasa at birth : Years 5–1–6.

The Fourth House.—Sagittarius the fourth house is a benefic sign. It is free from occupation but is aspected by Jupiter lord of the fourth and Mercury lord of Lagna and is thus considerably fortified. In the Navamsa, there is a slight afflicton of the fourth house which is negligible as fourth lord Mars aspects the fourth from his own sign Aries.

The Fourth Lord.—The fourth lord is in a kendra in association with Lagnadhipati Mercury. The moderate affliction to which Jupiter is subjected to in Navamsa is more than counterbalanced by his strong disposition in Rasi.

Matrukaraka.—The Moon is in Aries, a trikona from the fourth house and is aspected by exalted Saturn. Therefore the Moon's affliction is also feeble.

Conclusion.—Consequently the fourth house is quite strong rendering the native enjoy the fortune of possessing his mother till his age of 52.

Education and Learning

We shall now consider the combinations that make one learned. Acquisition of learning should be ascertained by a consideration of the fourth house and Jupiter. It must be noted that with the aid of astrology, as known at present it may not be possible to say from an examination of the horoscope whether one's inclinations would be for Physics or Chemistry, Engineering or Metallurgy.

The fault of course does not lie with astrology. It shows our own imperfections and how we have not cared to tap the original source of astrological knowledge, by a proper study and adaptation of which it would doubtless be posible to anticipate the exact type of education that one is likely to take to either for his livelihood or for the sake of knowledge. We are giving general combinations and a number of illustrations leaving the reader to pursue his own line of thought or argument to arrive at finer conclusions. From the classical works are culled out the following combinations indicative of inclinations towards different branches of learning.

Venus in the fourth makes one proficient in music. Mercury in the fourth makes one proficient in astrology. The Sun and the Moon similarly placed favour political science, psychology and metaphysics. Sun–Mercury combination favours proficiency in mathematics. Venus in the fourth, combined with Mercury or Sun, endows one with poetical instincts.

The Sun and Mars having anything to do with Mercury make one a logician. Jupiter similarly placed makes the person an expert in Vedas and Vedangas. Here the planet having to do most with the fourth house is to be considered and not merely the house or the lord. Thus if Venus is lord of the fourth and he is in the seventh with Mercury and Mars and the fourth is occupied by Saturn and the Moon, the person will be acquainted with different branches of learning. Consistent with the inherent nature and indications of the planet mainly connected with the fourth house, either as lord, occupant or associate, one has to infer the type of education one is likely to get. The Sun is the king and the ruler. The Moon represents a wavering mind. Mars is the warrior and the practical man. Mercury is the thinker and the adept. Jupiter is the priest, spiritualist and the judge. Venus is the poet and philosopher. Saturn is the statesman and leader. Rahu is a diplomat and Ketu is the prophet and the seer. With these clues, we have to interpret the horoscope, consistent with commonsense factors, if we have to perceive the truth of astrology. Astrology is a science. Studied and applied with the utmost integrity, astrology can be a real boon to humanity. The qualities and influencing abilities allotted to planets and signs must not be taken too literally. For example when we say that Venus is a planet of poetry, it does not mean that one visualise as poet singing through the heavens. It means simply that persons born at a time when Venus is situated in that portion of the heavens, which symbolically rules education, do tend to exhibit an aptitude for poetry, music and fine arts. When dealing with the tenth bhava in the second volume of this work, I propose to give adequate statistical data regarding the professions and occupations denoted by different planets. These data will also be helpful in finding out the educational and literary attainments. The laws of horoscopic interpretation are quite sound for, they are based upon the vast experience of astrological thinkers of all ages.

Chart No 76.—*Born on 12–2–1856 at about 12–21 p.m. (L.M.T.) (Lat. 18° N., Long. 84° E.)*

	Rahu Moon	Lagna	Sat.		Lagna Jupiter	Rahu	
Sun Merc. Jupit.							
	RASI			NAVAMSA			
Venus		Mars Ketu		Merc.	Ketu	Sun Venus Saturn Mars	Moon

Balance of Venus Dasa at birth : Years 12–3–9.

The Fourth House.—The fourth house is Leo. It is occupied by no planet. Saturn, Sun, Mercury and Jupiter aspect the fourth house. The Sun as lord of the fourth and Mercury as lord of the second and fifth aspecting the fourth house have fortified the house considerably.

Yogakaraka Saturn's aspect is equally important. Hence the fourth house is rendered quite strong.

The Fourth Lord.—The Sun is the fourth lord. He is in the tenth, in association with Mercury and Jupiter, owning the 2nd and 5th and 8th and 11th respectively. The Sun aspects the fourth house. Mercury's association with the fourth lord is highly significant.

Vidyakaraka.—Jupiter, the Vidyakaraka, aspects vidyasthana (fourth) and is well fortified but for his ownership of the 8th and 11th, which may be ignored for purposes of assessing Vidyabhava (house of education).

Conclusion.—The strong disposition of the house, the lord and the karaka or indicator conferred on the native high education—Jupiter and Mercury indicating proficiency in astrology, Jupiter denoting scholarship in law and Vedic learning and Saturn's aspect denoting great proficiency in English language and literature. Here an observation has to be made. Venus is the karaka for music. He is in the 9th from the Moon and in the 11th from Vidyakaraka. This explains the great interest the native evinced in music. The intellectual attainments of this subject were not confined to any particular field. He was a historian, astrologer, linguist, literateur and lawyer of no mean order. And his achievements in the field of learning are well borne out by the disposition and stength of the Vidyabhava and the karaka.

The Fourth House.—In Chart No. 77 the fourth house is Leo, unoccupied by any planet but aspected by Saturn. In the Navamsa the fourth house is aspected by Jupiter.

The Fourth Lord.—The fourth lord Sun is in Cancer in association with Venus lord of Lagna and aspected by Jupiter, the karaka for vidya. In the Navamsa also, the Sun joins Venus and Mars in the 7th from Lagna.

Vidyakaraka.—Jupiter, the Vidyakaraka, is in an ideal position. As lord of the 8th and 11th from Lagna and Chandra Lagna respectively, he is in the 11th in his own house aspected by Saturn the yogakaraka.

Chart No. 77.—*Born on 26-7-1856 A.D. at Midnight at Dublin.*

Rahu Jupit.		Lagna Moon	Merc. Sat.	Rahu Sat.		Lagna Moon	Merc.
			Sun Venus				
	RASI				NAVAMSA		
		Mars	Ketu	Jupit.	Sun Venus Mars		Ketu

Balance of Moon Dasa at birth : Years 6-6-18.

Conclusion.—The house, the lord and the karaka being fairly well disposed, endowed the native with considerable intellectual equipment. Vidyakaraka Jupiter in the eleventh and Mercury the planet of intelligence in the second is suggestive of financial gains and public favour through writing. Venus in conjunction with the fourth lord made him a successful music and art critic.

The Fourth House.—Leo is the fourth house. It is occupied by the mystic planet Ketu and aspected by the matter-of-fact planet Mars. In the Navamsa, the fourth is aspected by Jupiter.

The Fourth Lord.—The fourth lord Sun is in the 7th, a secret sign aspected by Jupiter and otherwise free from affliction. In the Navamsa again, the Sun is situated in Sagittarius aspected by Jupiter.

The Karaka —Jupiter the Vidyakaraka occupies the Lagna and is aspected by the lord of the fourth Sun.

Chart No. 78.—*Born on 30–11–1858 at A.D. 4–25 p.m. (L.M.T.) (Long. 90° 8′ E., Lat. 23° 33′ N.)*

		Lagna Jupiter				Mercury	Moon Venus
Rahu			Sat.				Mars Ketu
	RASI			Lagna Rahu Sat.	NAVAMSA		
Mars			Ketu				Jupit.
Venus Merc.	Sun		Moon	Sun			

Balance of Moon Dasa at birth : Years 2–3–0.

Conclusion.—All the three factors governing education and learning have been considerably fortified. The fourth being occupied by Ketu and aspected by Mars indicates that the subject was a visionary, yet steeped in matter-of-fact science. The native attained acknowledged distinction in Physics but his sphere of activities extended towards biology also.

The Fourth House.—In Chart No. 79 the fourth house is Capricorn and is free from affliction either by occupation or aspect. In the Navamsa, the fourth house has Jupiter posited in it aspected by exalted Venus.

The Fourth Lord.—Saturn, who owns the fourth and who is also Yogakaraka, is in Lagna, exalted. From Chandra Lagna, the fourth lord Venus (who also happens to be Yogakaraka in this case) is in the eighth from the

Chart No. 79.—*Born on 28-8-1749 at 12-17 p.m. (L.M.T.) (Long. 8° 41' E., Lat.50° 3' N.)*

Jupit.		Ketu	Venus	Moon	Saturn	Lagna Ketu Merc.
Moon	NAVAMSA	Sun Merc.		RASI		Sun Mars
Mars Rahu	Lagna Saturn	Venus	Rahu			Jupit.

Balance of Jupiter Dasa at birth : Years 12–4–24.

Moon, having obtained neechabhanga and causing Adhi Yoga. In the Navamsa again, the fourth lord Mercury is in Lagna, in his own house.

Karaka.—Jupiter is in his own house in an Upachaya from Lagna and the second from Chandra Lagna aspected by Venus. In the Navamsa the fourth lord and Vidyakarka are in mutual kendras.

Conclusion.—Chart No 16 belongs to one of the greatest poets of Europe of the eighteenth century. Mark how the influences of Venus, Jupiter and Saturn have blended together in relation to the house of learning and how all these three planets have been strengthened either by association or occupation of own house. The native of the horoscope was also interested in astrology, philosophy, art and metaphysical and mystical writings. The situation of Jupiter in the fourth in the Navamsa and exalted Venus aspecting the fourth are significant combinations suggestive of the emotions that moulded the native's poetical thoughts.

Chart No. 80.—*Born on 7-9-1856 at 4 p.m. (L.M.T.)*
(Long. 5h. 10m. 20s. E., Lat. 13° N.)

Jupit. Rahu			Sat.		Mercury	Lagna Sat.
			Venus Rahu			Mars
	RASI			NAVAMSA		
Lagna			Sun	Moon		Ketu
	Moon Mars		Venus Merc. Ketu		Jupiter	Sun

Balance of Mercury Dasa at birth : Years 10-1-17.

The Fourth House.—The fourth house is Aries and is unafflicted.

The Fourth Lord.—The fourth lord Mars is in the eleventh (eighth from the fourth) in association with debilitated Moon and aspected by Jupiter. In the Navamsa, the fourth lord Mercury is in the twelfth aspected by Jupiter.

Vidyakaraka.—Though Vidyakaraka Jupiter is in his own sign, yet he is considerably afflicted by Rahu and is aspected by Saturn and debilitated Venus.

Conclusion.—Vidyakaraka's affliction resulted in the native getting very ordinary school education. But the fairly strong disposition of the fourth house and the lord rendered him acquire knowledge of men and matters and the native occupied a very high official position in life. There are, of course, several Rajayogas in this horoscope and it is beyond the scope of the present observations.

Education, in common parlance, means the acquisition of certain distinctions having undergone the necessary courses of study in recognised institutions and not the acquisition of knowledge by self-study.

Chart No. 81.—*Born on 23–11–1902 at 5–16 a.m. (L.M.T.) (Lat. 23° 8' N., Long. 72° 40' E.)*

	Ketu				Ketu Mandi	Lagna	Merc.
	RASI		Mandi Moon Mars		**NAVAMSA**		Jupit.
Jupit. Sat.				Sat.			Moon
	Venus Sun	Rahu Lagna Mercury			Mars	Rahu	Sun Venus

Balance of Venus Dasa at birth : Years 13–11–12.

The Fourth House.—In Chart No. 81, Capricorn becomes the fourth. It is occupied by Saturn and Jupiter, the latter in neecha but having obtained neechabhanga. In the Navamsa, the fourth is free from association or aspect.

The Fourth Lord.—The fourth lord Saturn, happening also to be Yogakaraka, is in the fourth, in association with Jupiter lord of the 3rd and the 6th.

Vidyakaraka.—Jupiter is subjected to all the influences to which Satun is. Jupiter is exalted in the Navamsa.

Conclusion.—Mark the strong disposition of all the three factors and especially the dignified positions of both the lord and the karaka. From Chandra Lagna, th-

fourth becomes strengthened by the situation of Venus and
the Sun (lord of Chandra Lagna) further aspected by Mars
lord of the fourth. Consistent with the dominant positions of Mars and Saturn, the subject was a professor.
Jupiter's strong disposition has rendered the native an
authority on Power-Engineering.

The Fourth House.—In Chart No. 82, the fourth is
Leo, a fixed sign and it is occupied by the Moon, lord of
the third and hence blemished. It is aspected by Mercury,
lord of the fifth. In the Navamsa, the fourth house is
Scorpio. It is occupied by Mars, the lord, and aspected
by Saturn, a malefic.

Chart No 82.—*Born on 16-3-1908 at 10-56 a.m.*
(I.S.T.) (Lat. 12° 2' N., Long. 75° 39' E.)

Sun Sat.	Mars Venus	Lagna	Rahu	Rahu		
Merc.			Jupit. Mandi			Moon
	RASI				AMSA	Lagna Sun Venus
			Moon			
Ketu				Mandi Merc.	Mars	Jupiter	Sat. Ketu

Balance of Ketu Dasa at birth :   Year 0–0–13.

The Fourth Lord.—The Sun owning the fourth is in a
benefic sign in association with Saturn and aspected by
exalted Jupiter.

The Vidyakaraka.—Jupiter is exalted in the third;
while in the Navamsa he is in the third.

13

Conclusion.—It is the Vidyakaraka that is really strong. The natives's general education in the sense of school knowledge is poor. His knowledge of English is almost nil. This is indicated by the Sun's (lord of the fourth) conjunction with Saturn. But, however, his grasp of the current political, social and international problems is unique. He is educated in the sense that he has learnt things by self-study and not by going to college or school.

Above we have given six charts bearing on education and learning. Each combination is capable of producing a variety of effects consistent with the ownerships, inherent and acquired natures and associations of the planets in Combination. Consequently in the analysis of a combination with a view to ascertaining a particular signification or event, all the factors having a bearing on the bhava have got to be considered.

Our humble experience suggests that for proficiency in music, Venus should be in the fourth or ninth or fifth house or aspect these houses. Interest in music may be predicted if Venus is in the fourth from the Moon. For proficiency in astrology, Mercury should be in the fourth, the Sun should be in the fifth or the Sun and Mercury should be in the second. The reference in all these caess is from Lagna or Chandra Lagna. Great learning in Vedas and other scriptures, consistent with the native's religion, can be predicted if the Sun and Mercury are in the fifth or Jupiter exalted or Jupiter occupies the second, ninth, fifth or tenth. Rahu's position in the fourth or fifth generally favours diplomacy. One who has this combination can probe into the minds of others and understand their mental currents. Students of Astrology should collect a large number of horoscopes and study the combinations in the light of actual results.

Conveyances and Possessions

The fourth house represents vehicles or carriages. We must also note the influences of the significator or karaka of conveyances, *viz.*, Venus. One of the important combinations for the acquisition or possession of a vehicle is the association of the lords of the fourth and ninth in Lagna or the seventh from Lagna. Venus in the fourth with the lord of the fourth or in the eleventh confers ordinary vehicles. The fourth lord in conjunction with the Moon or Venus as lord of the fourth (which is possible if Lagna is Aquarius or Cancer) in the eleventh, tenth or ninth indicates possession of vehicles. Vahanakaraka is Venus and Vahanasthana is fourth. It is by a consideration of these factors *plus* the fourth lord that we have to predict Vahana Yoga. Even in possession of Vahanas or conveyances, there are gradations. A streamlined limousine cannot be equated with a push bike or a bullock-cart though all of them fall under the category of Vahanas. Jupiter's presence in or aspect of the fourth *plus* the situation of Venus in the seventh is a sure indication of the acquisition of a fitting Vahana. In this connection, I would refer the readers to Chapter IV of my English translation of BHAVARTHA RATNAKARA, wherein several combinations have been given, indicative of the acquisition of Vahanas or vehicles.

Regarding the possession of houses, the strangling hut and the more exquisitely furnished mansion, fall in the same category. It is only a difference of degree. It is the inherent strengths, the afflictions, the fortified positions of the karakas and the appropriate lord that reveal whether one would acquire a hut or a palace. The following combinations indicate possession of houses. Lord of Lagna or the seventh joining Lagna or the fourth; strong disposition of the fourth lord in exaltation or kendra; the

lord of the fourth occupying the shashtiamsas of Gopura,
Mridwa or Simhasana; Vahanakaraka posited in his own
Thrimsamsa; lords of the fourth and tenth in association
in a kendra; and Venus strongly posited in the fourth. In
applying the above combinations, the astrologer must use
his skill and "the skill of the astrologer" as Prof. B.
Suryanarain Rao says must be "consistent with interpretation and comprehension of these minutes".

Chart No. 83.—*Born on 12-3-1863 at 2-3 a.m. (Lat.
22° 20' N., Long. 4h. 53m. E.)*

Venus	Mars Ketu		Mars Saturn		Sun
Sun Merc.					Ketu
	RASI			AMSA	
			Venus Rahu		
Lagna	Moon Rahu	Jupiter	Sat.	Jupit. Moon	Mercury	Lagna

Balance of Mercury Dasa at birth: Years 14–7–6.

The above chart is simple. The fourth lord Jupiter is
in the eleventh while the fourth house is occupied by
exalted Venus. Again, from Chandra Lagna the fourth
Lord Saturn is in the eleventh and the fourth is aspected by
Jupiter, the fifth lord, and occupied by the tenth lord.
The subject possessed not one, but many luxurious conveyances and mansions throughout life.

Chart no. 84 is a typical horoscope illustrating the
possession of innumerable houses and vehicles. Mark the
fact that the fourth lord Saturn is in the eleventh with

Chart No. 84.—*Born on 30–7–1863 at 2 p.m. (Lat. 42° 5' N., Long. 83° 5' W.)*

	Ketu		Saturn Ketu		Mars
		Sun Merc.			Lagna Moon
RASI			AMSA		
Moon		Mars	Venus		
	Lagna Rahu	Sat. Jupit. Venus		Sun	Rahu Mercury	Jupit.

Balance of Moon Dasa at birth : Years 2–4–29.

Jupiter, lord of the second and fifth, and Venus, lord of the seventh. Venus Vahanakaraka has Neechabhanga, while Mars Grihakaraka not only happens to be Lagnadhipathi but aspects the fourth from the tenth.

In Chart No. 85 lord of Lagna Saturn is in the fourth. The fourth lord Venus is in the seventh with Mercury lord of the fifth. Lords of the fourth and tenth are in association in the seventh. Both the karakas of house and vehicles are in the fourth from the Moon. Note the native acquired a fine car in Jupiter Dasa Venus Bhukti and a decent house in Jupiter Dasa Mars Bhukti.

In Chart No. 86 the fourth house is Virgo and it is occupied by the 3rd lord Sun and aspected by Saturn lord of the 8th. The fourth lord Mercury is equally afflicted. The native enjoyed for some time the luxury of owning a car but he had to dispense not only with his car but a fine job also as his spendthrift nature and speculative tendencies landed him in endless troubles and he was pursued day

Chart No. 85.—*Born on 8-8-1912 A.D. at 7-35 p.m. (I.S.T.) (Lat. 13° N., Long. 5h. m. 20s. E.)*

Rahu		Moon Saturn				Saturn	Venus
Lagna			Sun	Sun Rahu			
	RASI		Mars Merc. Venus	Lagna	AMSA		Moon Merc. Ketu
	Jupiter		Ketu			Jupiter	Mars

Balance of Mars Dasa at birth : Years 6-1-6.

Chart No. 86.—*Born on 26-9-1901 at 12-20 a.m. (L.M.T.) (Lat. 10° 25' N., Long. 5h. 53m. E.)*

	Ketu		Lagna	Venus	Sun Lagna	Mars Rahu	
Moon							Jupit.
	RASI				AMSA		
Jupit. Sat.	Rahu Mercury Mars Venus	Sun		Moon	Ketu	Mercury	Sat.

Balance of Rahu Dasa at birth : Years 16-1-18.

in and day out by his creditors. To escape the clutches
of his creditors, the native has been roaming about here
and there, torn away from his family and children.
Mercury's association with Mars–Rahu is solely responsible for his speculative tendencies and losses.

Chart No. 87.—*Born on 28-8-1909 at 9-52 a.m.
(L.M.T.) (Lat. 13° N., Long. 77° 35' E.)*

Mars	Saturn	Rahu			Saturn	Venus	
	RASI		Sun Jupit. Mandi	Moon Lagna Ketu Merc.	AMSA		Rahu
Moon							
	Ketu	Lagna	Merc. Venus	Jupit.	Mars Mandi		Sun

Balance of Sun Dasa at birth : Years 3-7-20.

The fourth is Capricorn a movable sign aspected by
Saturn the lord. The fourth is occupied by the Moon
lord of the tenth. The fourth lord is considerably afflicted
by being neecha and subjected to Papakarthari Yoga. He
is, of course, aspected by Jupiter, who being lord of the
third and sixth is himself afflicted. From Chandra Lagna
again, the fourth is occupied by debilitated Saturn and
the lord happens to be in the twelfth from fourth.
Vahanakaraka is neecha while Grihakaraka is weak. The
subject is a Police Jamedar drawing about Rs. 60 per
mensum. None of the indications of the forth house

have been conferred on him consistent with the intensely
malefic disposition of the house.

Hundreds of examples can be given to prove the
astrological dictum that the fourth house *plus* the appropriate karaka should be well disposed to assure an optimum
share of the significations.

8. The Fifth House

The fifth house refers to children, emotions and feelings, faith in God and Poorvapunya. To a certain extent it is also concerned with speculative tendencies. The remarks made in para 2 of page 159 pertaining to the fourth house apply with equal force to the fifth house also.

Main Considerations

In analysing the fifth bhava, due consideration must be given to the three important factors, *viz., (a)* the house, *(b)* the lord, and *(c)* the karaka, which in this case would be Jupiter. There are the secondary considerations, *viz.,* the occupants of the fifth house, the associates joining the fifth lord and the karaka and the Yogakaraka, *i.e ,* the planets causing the various yogas bearing on the fifth house.

Before considering the general combinations, we shall make a few observations on the emotional side of nature as revealed by the fifth house. Some sign of the zodiac would be on the bhavamadhya of the fifth house. Consistent with the nature of this sign and blended by the nature of the planet or planets situated therein or aspecting the sign, the emotional nature of the native will be developed. When Agnitatwa Rasis or fiery signs (Aries, Leo and Sagittarius) have reference to the fifth house, the native cannot be corrupt unless the horoscope has other unfavourable attributes. The native possesses vivid idiosyncracies. He takes everything in the world seriously and possesses a sense of importance. In excess, this independence of spirit, characteristic of this tatwa, can be offensive in relation to other people. This becomes the case when the bhava-madya falls exactly in a fiery constellation or Mars occupies the fifth. When not afflicted, the person faces life with courage and the mind voyages through the strange seas of thought alone. Unless the Moon is away from this combination, emotion is life to the person. His marked trait would be that he can forgive almost anything excepting a fool. The quality of stupidity makes him indignant. However, there exist softer and milder types of the same central character. A literary writer, in whom this element is strong, excels in developing an idea. The mind travels too far afield. There is little sequence of ideas or sense of structure and the general effect is illogical. One with Leo on the 5th house possesses a quite divine foresight with regard to future. Generosity is a marked characteristic. A lady born under such a set-up has the knack of proving an ideal housewife. She is impressive in action. Summing up, a fiery sign on the fifth house gives that ardent, fiery quality which inspires and invigorates one with the energy to act. It is dynamic and forceful, aspiring and inspiring. It saves one from being sunk in the inner seas of emotion or lost in the airy heights of abstract thought.

If the Bhutatwa Rasis or earthly signs (Taurus, Capricorn and Virgo) are in the 5th house, the person will possess a retentive memory, imagination and deep feeling. He has an attraction for hidden things. He is difficult to deal with as he is elusive, trifle, impish, stubborn and somewhat peevish. If the fifth bhava is in Taurus, the person will be highly optimistic and he takes life easy.

The opposite holds good for Capricorn. He will be highly pessimistic and takes life rather too seriously. If the sign is Virgo then there will be a blending of the characteristics of Taurus and Capricorn. The earthy element makes the person take a mystical view of physical life. This element is intuitional and psychic. Another fundamental quality is retrospection and exquisite sensibility often elevated to a mystical belief in an inner life within the forms and objects of nature. Criticism and censure closely allied to active kindness and helpfulness, obstinacy, a certain irritability, closeness over money and jealousy, in love, are some of the important characteristics of this group.

The Vayutatwa Rasis (airy signs), *viz.*, Gemini, Libra and Aquarius on the 5th house, give rise to an altogether different emotional set-up. The Vayutatva element is concerned with conduct rather than motive, with action rather than thought or feeling. One characteristic of a person born under this set-up is his liking for the ordinary and familiar—the insignificant things in life, humble everyday people and simple annals of the poor. Libra is the most practical while Aquarius is the least matter-of-fact. Gemini hits at the golden mean. We have of course to consider the collective influences focussed on the fifth house and then come to a conclusion. Usually shrewd and far-seeing, one born with a Vayutatwa Rasi in the fifth house is an innate philosopher. However much disturbed, he has the capacity to remain calm and settle into poise. In general outlook the philosophy is that of determinism and the work is often shadowed by a dark sense of fate. The past is looked upon and valued chiefly as a fact and not as a cherished memory. He observes tradition and convention. He upholds existing laws and conditions in religion and philosophy. At its very highest

it becomes a grave acceptance of some power ordering
human lives, a submission to the inevitable and to a noble
resignation to the outworking of universal laws. The
virtues of this group are discipline and restraint, its ideals
obedience and sobriety. Often in the case of Aquarius,
there is associated a certain seriousness of outlook and a
gravity of tone—the former being at times a heavy melancholy. Summing up, one born with a Vayutatwa Rasi on
the 5th possesses the commonsense necessary to rule the
world. He is awake to realities. He has his own virtues
and qualities which no other elements can give. He makes
us realise that facts are facts which we must face and
accept—not run away from or try to distort.

If the fifth house falls in a Jalatatwa Rasi (Cancer,
Scorpio and Pisces), it indicates an attitude of mind where
balance is the dominant element. The person will possess
an impartiality of outlook, a kindly tolerance and a
philosophy of moderation, poise and a sense of proportion. There is also a certain amount of satire and a
mixture of jest and earnest. The mental disposition is one
of quieter but more persistent effort. Scorpio has a sting
in its tail and this is the thing to watch out against.

The person will be uncompromising, exacting, fault-
finding. Yet he can display keen judgment and power of
imparital criticism. The wisdom of the serpent lies concealed. Tenacity is one of his chief characteristics. He
will display sympathy, persistence, emotion and be somewhat self-possessed and self-reliant.

When Pisces is in the fifth bhava, the person will have a
restless but a creative mind with an imaginative outlook.
He is liable to be obsessed with curious fancies. The
characteristics of a person born under this set-up are
difficult to interpret with any degree of clearness. He
always pretends to be different from what he really is and

there will be an over-abundance of self-esteem and appro-bativeness combined. Summing up, the imagination is fertile and the nature resourceful and there is much pride in the mental disposition.

It must be noted that the above characteristics are said to be conferred provided a Rasi belonging to a certain tatwa is in the fifth house. The exact mental set-up depends upon the combined influences of the exact Rasi *plus* the planetary and constellation influences. Though Cancer, Scorpio and Pisces belong to the same category, yet each has got its own distinctive characteristics to impress. It is here that the astrologer is called upon to use his power of judgment.

Results of the Lord of the Fifth House being placed in Different Houses

In the First House.—If the 5th lord is favourably combined and associated, the person commands a number of servants, becomes a Judge, Magistrate or Minister empowered to punish the evil-minded. He will earn the grace of God ; few children ; will have foes and gives happiness to others. If the 5th lord is afflicted, there will be no issues ; will invoke kshudra devatas (evil and destruc-tive forces), will be evil-minded and leader of a gang of deceitful persons ; a tale-bearer with a sting. If the lord is moderately good, mixed results will follow.

In the Second House. If the 5th lord is favourably disposed, the person will be blessed with a beautiful wife and well-behaving children. There will be gains from Government or King. He will become learned and a good astrologer. Lord weak and afflicted, Poor ; loss of money through Government displeasure ; will be unable to maintain his own family ; will have family troubles and misunderstandings ; becomes a priest in a Siva temple.

In the Third House.—Favourably disposed, many good children and brothers, If unfavourably disposed, loss of children, misunderstandings with brothers and continuous occupational troubles. He will become stingy and a tale bearer.

In the Fourth House.—If favourably disposed, the person will have a few sons, one of whom will live by agriculture. The mother will live long. May become an adviser to a ruler or his preceptor. The lord, afflicted, causes death of children. The lord, moderately strong, confers daughters and no sons.

In the Fifth House.—Lord favourably disposed indicates a number of sons; becomes great in his own line of activity; otherwise he becomes an expert in Mantrasastra and befriends persons in power. He may also become an expert in mathematics or head of a religious institution. Lord afflicted, contrary results should be anticipated. Children will die; he will not keep to his word; wavering mentality and cruel.

In the Sixth House.—If the fifth lord is favourably disposed, the maternal uncle will be a famous man. He will have enmity with his own son. If the lord is afflicted, issues will not be born and he may have to adopt one from maternal uncle's line.

In the Seventh House.—When the lord is favourably disposed, the native's son lives abroad and attains distinction, wealth and fame. Or he will have a number of issues. He will also become renowned, learned, prosperous, greatly devoted to his master and possesses a charming personality. When the lord is afflicted, there will be loss of children, one of whom will die abroad after attaining name and fame.

In the Eighth House.—Paternal property will be lost due to debts. There will be extinction of the family. He will suffer from lung troubles. He will be peevish, unhappy but not poor.

In the Ninth House.—He will become a teacher or a preceptor. Renovates ancient temples, wells, choultries and gardens. One of the sons attains distinction as an orator or author. If the lord is afflicted, he will earn divine wrath and consequent destruction of fortune.

In the Tenth House.—If the lord is beneficially disposed, a Raja Yoga is formed. Acquires landed property ; earns the goodwill of the rulers, constructs temples and performs religious sacrifices ; one of the sons becomes a gem of the family. If aspected by the Sun the native may join the intelligence department. If the lord is afflicted, faces the wrath of the rulers and contrary results will happen.

In the Eleventh House.—Benefits through sons and success in all undertakings ; becomes rich and learned and helps others ; will have a number of sons ; becomes an author.

In the Twelfth House.—Quest for knowing the Ultimate Reality will be pronounced. He will lead a life of non-attachment, becomes spiritual, moves from one place to another and ultimately attains Moksha.

It will be seen that the above combinations are quite general and they have to be used with great care paying particular attention to the benefic, malefic, or moderating nature of the lord qualified or modified otherwise by the association or aspect of the other planets and lords.

Important Combinations

The following combinations bearing on the fifth house have been culled out from important sources, and they are general in character requiring the skill and intelligence of the astrologer for their correct interpretation and explanation.

If the fifth house has beneficial associations or aspects, there will be children. Lord of the Lagna in the fifth and the fifth lord strong, or exchange of houses between first and fifth lords, favours birth of children. If Jupiter, as lord of the fifth, is strong and aspected by lord of Lagna, one gets many issues. Lord of the 2nd, possessed of strength, in the fifth, aspected by Jupiter, indicates birth of children. Birth of children is also indicated when the lord of the Navamsa occupied by the owner of the fifth be conjoined with or aspected by a benefic or when the lord of the fifth is in benefic amsas or when the lord of the Navamsa occupied by the lord of the fifth is in Lagna bhava.

Children will die early if the lord of the fifth occupies 3, 6 or 12 and is aspected by no benefic; when the lord of the fifth is hemmed in between malefics; when the fifth is aspected by a malefic, the lord of the fifth joins an evil planet; when the lord of the 5th occupies cruel and debilitated Navamsas; when the lord of the Drekkana, or the Navamsa, joined by the lord of the twelfth aspects the 5th lord; when Rahu occupying the 5th is aspected by Mars when Saturn aspected by the Moon occupies the 5th and the lord of the 5th joins Rahu; when Rahu and lord of Lagna are associated with the 5th lord or occupy the 5th.

The family is extinguished when the lord of Lagna is in the 5th, and Lagna and the Moon have evil associations when the fifth is occupied by Mercury and the Lagna by a malefic; when malefics occupy the 1st, 5th, 8th and 12th houses or the 5th house exclusively and when Mars Saturn and the Sun occupy respectively the 1st, 8th and 5th houses. The first child will be male, if the 5th lord in the 1st, 2nd or 3rd or if Mars, Venus and Moon are in common signs, Sagittarius excepted. One would have no child living if Venus is in the 7th, Moon is in the tenth and evil planets are in the 5th from the lord of the 5th. Male children will be got if lord of 5th is in the houses of Moon or Venus, aspected or joined by them. The first child dies if Mars is in the 5th aspected by Jupiter or Venus. One gets a child in his 32nd year if Jupiter is in the 5th and lord of 5th is with Venus.

An obedient child is born if the 5th lord aspects or occupies the ascendant and lord of Lagna is similarly disposed towards the 5th. A disobedient child is born if the 5th lord is afflicted and unaspected by Lagnadhipati but seen by Mars or Rahu. Lagna being Aries or Scorpio, and the Sun and Saturn placed in the 5th and 8th respectively influenced by a benefic, the person will have children late in life. If the 5th house falls in Gemini, Virgo, Capricorn or Aquarius and has the association of Saturn or Mandi, one will have an adopted son. When a malefic is in the eleventh house and the Moon and Venus occupy the 5th, the first-born will be a daughter. The person will have three children if the Sun aspected by a benefic occupies the 5th, or Virgo being Lagna and Saturn is in the 5th : five children if Libra is Lagna and Saturn is in the 5th. If the lords of the 1st and the 5th aspect each other, the son will be obedient to the father. Saturn, Mercury and the Moon in the 5th make one 'purchase' a son for the continuance of the family.

Jupiter in the 5th gives good intellect and memory. Rahu and Saturn in the 5th make one dull and stupid.

Planets in the Fifth House

The Sun.—This combination deprives the person of children, riches and happiness. His life will be short. He will suffer from heart disease, will roam about in forest

14

regions; a mountaineer. This position also denotes difficult child-birth.

The Moon.—Clarity of mind, happiness from children, acquisition of lands, gems and precious stones, opportunity to serve the State are indicated when the Moon is in the 5th. The person will be straightforward, truthful, learned, gentlemanly, god-fearing, and devoid of enemies. Strong tendency towards speculation is also denoted. One of the children becomes famous.

Mars.—Miserable for his wife, friends and children; always disturbed in thoughts; impressive, rash, weak-minded, back-biter and unhappy. He will suffer from colic and suffers misfortunes through children. Too much attached to sex pleasures and consequently loss of health. Dangerous child-birth may be predicted in a woman's chart.

Mercury.—Learned and happy, will have a number of children. The person may become an adviser or a minister; highly intelligent and learned in Mantrasastras; inclined to too much of sex pleasure and consequently lacking in vitality.

Jupiter.—Learned in logic and law, mantrasastra, highly intelligent, preceptor or adviser to a king and great discriminating power. He will have good friends and vehicles and decorous manners. A number of children; god-fearing; happy with children and friends.

Venus.—Poetic; possesses a number of friends and beautiful children; happiness through offspring; wise and discriminating; acquires wealth; respected by the State. This position also indicates more of female children and success in speculation.

Saturn.—Evil-minded and stupid; sickly and weak; poor and hated by others. This combination denotes sorrows through children. Fortune will be variable and not steady and he will have a hyprocritical nature. Quarrels with friends and relatives and sorrow in domestic life.

Rahu.—Suffers from colic ; mistaken by others and unfriended ; will lose a number of children ; hard-hearted and unconventional ; heart trouble.

Ketu.—Loss of children ; trouble in the stomach, strange and peculiar experiences in connection with emotions and feelings. Later on in life, inclination towards spirituality.

The above results get modified by the aspects and associations of other lords. If the Sun is afflicted, there will be loss through speculation and trouble with cousins. If the Moon joins malefics or is aspected by them, there will be loss through children and loose sex relations. If the afflicting planet be Mars, children die after some time. If the afflicting planet is Saturn, there is fear of brain derangement. The 5th house is an index to the lower human feelings. Moon afflicted by Mars in this position denotes intrigues and loose sex relations. Affliction of Mars denotes danger of ruin and disgrace through the opposite sex. If Mars is strengthened, there will be gains through lands, chemicals and factories. Trouble and danger through children are shown. There will be inclination to rush into rash speculations. Mercury afflicted gives anxiety and worry through children. If afflicted by Mars there will be a scandal in connection with love affairs. The emotional side of nature dominates the reason. If well aspected by Jupiter, it favours gain through speculation and authorship.

If Jupiter is strengthened, life will be smooth. If afflicted, troubles arise consistent with the nature of the afflicting planet. Venus well fortified denotes

gains through females and extra marital attachments
with actresses or singers. If afflicted, there will be
loss of health through over-indulgence. If Mars is
the afflicting planet, there will be indiscriminate bes-
towal of affection on children. Rahu afflicting gives
strange courtships. Saturn afflicting gives disappointments in love affairs. Saturn afflicted by Mars
denotes danger of unnatural attachments, especially
to those who are older. There will be loss of children,
danger of drowning and even heart trouble. If
Saturn's position is strengthened by Jupiter, gains in
mines is indicated.

Rahu's affliction is a very bad combination. It
causes scandal through children. If Venus associates
with Rahu, there may be homo-sexual tendencies.
Ketu afflicted gives criminal tendencies. The person
lacks even a sense of shame when provoked and
usually possesses a vindictive nature. The native
lacks the human touch in his approach towards one
or two of the issues. If Venus joins Kethu, the man
chooses platonic love. If the afflicting planet is
Mars, many dangers are threatened and the family
will be extinguished. Much skill is required in judging
the 5th house and in interpreting the various combinations.

Time of Fructification of the Results of the Fifth House

Careful attention to the methods suggested in
previous chapters for interpretation of time-factors
in regard to the fructification of the results of the
bhavas dealt with therein will enable any intelligent
person to anticipate the probable period in which
events pertaining to the 5th house take place. To
analyse a bhava and to indicate the likely period of

fructification of events, a true sense of proportion and discrimination is needed on the part of the astrological student. The laws of interpretation, based on vast experience, should be carefully studied and understood. First attempts may prove disappointing and discouraging, but subsequent attempts are bound to succeed. Failure may be due to overlooking some point.

As we have said above, the 5th house has mainly to do with issues and secondarily with intelligence, emotions and fame. We have to consider whether the native is likely to enjoy the Dasa of the 5th lord during his lifetime. If there is no chance of the Dasa of the 5th lord being enjoyed, then we have to find out the planets which will influence the 5th house by way of occupation and aspect and whether the native will enjoy the Dasa of such planets.

In timing events pertaining to the 5th house, the following factors have to be noted :—

(a) The lord, (b) the planet or planets aspecting the 5th house, (c) planet or planets posited in the 5th house, (d) planets aspecting the lord of the 5th house, (e) planet or planets in association with the lord of the 5th house, (f) the lord of the 5th from the Moon and the karaka of the 5th bhava.

The factors above mentioned are capable of influencing the 5th house, either as lords of main periods (Dasas) or as lords of sub-periods (Bhuktis) or as lords of still minor periods.

The sub–periods of planets capable of influencing the 5th house, in the major periods of planets capable of influencing the 5th produce results pertaining to the 5th house *par excellence*. The sub-periods of planets associated with the house, in the major periods of planets not associated with the 5th house produce results pertaining to the 5th house to a limited extent only. Similarly the sub-periods of lords, who have nothing to do with the 5th in major periods of lords associated with 5th, will produce effects pertaining to fifth only to a limited or nominal extent,

Nature of Results

In general, the following results may be anticipated in the Dasas and Bhuktis of planets capable of influencing the fifth house, subject of course to the peculiarities of the individual horoscope concerned.

The 5th lord in his own house or otherwise strong: there will be birth of sons and favour from superiors. Misunderstandings with the sons will be the result if the 5th lord in Lagna has an adverse Navamsa position. If the 5th lord occupies the 6th in association with the 6th lord, the native's maternal uncle will prosper or the native will derive benefits from the maternal uncle. If a politician, he will get political power. If the 5th lord has the above situation, but in the Navamsa is in the 6th, 8th or 12th from the place occupied by the 6th lord, there will be destruction of prosperity and he will be the victim of his ruler's wrath. When the influences are mixed, the results will also be mixed.

When the 5th lord is in the seventh in association with the seventh lord, the native will be benefited by his son's trip to and residence in foreign countries. There will be financial benefits and the native will enjoy the company of learned and pious persons. If not already married, marriage takes place and a new family will be set up. The 5th lord afflicted, misfortunes befall children.

When the 5th lord is in the 8th with the 8th lord, there will be death of children or abortions to wife, misunderstandings with kith and kin, displeasure of superiors and rulers and loss in business. The person will quarrel with his father and hate his family deity. When the 8th lord is afflicted or when the 5th lord is in the 6th, 8th or 12th (in Navamsa) from the 8th lord, the evil results will be considerably minimised.

When the 5th lord is in the ninth in association with the 9th lord and the lord of Lagna weak and joining the ninth, the person will have happiness from father during his boyhood or during the Dasa of the 5th lord. There will be inheritance of paternal or ancestral property, or he will get a good administrative or honorary post. The father will be in the good books of the ruling classes. When the 5th lord is very strong, there will be unexpected dawn of prosperity and fortune. This will be the case only if the 5th lord is Mars or the 5th house happens to be a sign of Mars. If the 5th lord is the Sun or Leo happens to be the 9th house, the person will become an author of religious books. There will be acquisition of wealth through a new administrative job, one's own occupation, and through female sources if the 5th lord is the Moon, Jupiter and Venus respectively or the 9th happens to be a sign ruled by one of the above three planets.

When the 5th lord is in the tenth in conjunction with the 10th lord or is in Lagna with the lord of Lagna, or in Navamsa Lagna, or the 5th and 10th lords are in Lagna, during the sub-period of the 10th lord, in the major period of the 5th lord, or in the sub-periods of Lagnadhipati, in the major period of the 5th lord, the person will acquire a kingdom or become head of a State, or a Minister, consistent with the strength of the lords concerned. When the lords have attained Vargottamamsa, the position acquired will be that of a king or head of a State. When the 5th lord is strongly disposed, as indicated above, but the Lagna lord is weak, Raja Yoga, during the Dasa of the 5th lord, will be enjoyed by the son.

In the assessment of the above yoga, the occupation of the person concerned should be carefully considered. A politician may become head of a State or Minister. One in Government service will reach the highest position. A businessman will have his palmy days while an agriculturist will earn enormous profits in his own avocation. In Interpreting horoscopes, commonsense must be applied to the blending of various indications.

When the 5th lord is in the 11th with the 11th lord, there will be acquisition of riches and gains from business. If in addition to the above disposition of the 5th lord, the 2nd lord is in deep exaltation in Rasi or in Navamsa, immense wealth and fortune will flow in. He will earn through sea-products or ship-building when the 5th house is a movable and watery sign. Consistent with the nature and characteristics of planets and signs involved, there will be influx of wealth.

When the 5th lord is in the 11th with the 11th lord, there will be gain through his sons or Government sources or elder brother, or one will acquire a new job. As the Dasa of the 5th lord, when in the 11th with the 11th lord, is a Yoga Dasa, it is capable of conferring highly beneficial results. When the 5th lord is in adverse amsas cantrary results may be expected. There will be losses in business, reverses in official life, disappointments, misunderstandings and financial troubles and upheavals.

When the lord of the 5th joins the lord of the 12th in the 12th (along with the 6th lord) there will be mental afflictions almost bordering on lunacy. Misunderstandings will arise with father and sons. He will incur the displeasure of the rulers. In the absence of the 6th lord in the above combination, the person becomes wiser and spends money on deserving causes.

When the lord of the 5th is in Lagna with the lord of Lagna, one becomes a leader of his community or a political party consistent with the nature of the planets concerned. He will acquire riches and conveyances. When the Dasa operates during childhood, he will be adopted into a rich family. If in the middle of life, the native will have good progeny. When the 5th lord occupies the 6th, 8th or 12th from the Lagnadhipati, in the Navamsa, contrary results should be expected. When strongly disposed, the 5th lord, in the above combination, is also capable of conferring during his Dasa *mantrasiddhi.* The person may also take to some religious or ascetic order.

When the 5th lord is in the 2nd with the 2nd lord, there will be domestic happiness and the person will develop power of eloquence.

When the 5th lord is in the 3rd in association with the 3rd lord, birth of children must be predicted in the subperiod of the 3rd lord within the major period of the 5th lord. The younger brother becomes famous and gets a good political or social position. The important results that may manifest during this Dasa are acquisition of strength of mind, courage and personality.

When the 5th lord is in the 4th with 4th lord, one will acquire a new conveyance and happiness through the ruling classes. When the 5th lord is weak, there will be loss of issues. He may incur the wrath of the Government and suffer its displeasure. When the lords of the 5th and 4th are strong, the native will have visits from eminent persons and caquisition of immovable property. If these two lords are very strong, he will acquire political power and will control the destinies of his country.

In this way, the results likely to happen during the Dasa of the 5th lord should be anticipated skilfully, taking into consideration the blends of strength and weakness the planet concerned is subject to.

As the 5th house has mainly to do with fecundity, birth of children, their prosperity, and adversity and happiness or misery from them, we shall study a number of charts illustrative of the combinations bearing on children. In studying the 5th house, it is essential that the horoscopes of both the husband and wife are considered from the point of view of fertility or sterility.

Science holds that masculine impotence, though of a physical character as a phenomenon, is very frequently determined by psychical factors. The sexual hypochondria is supposed to frequently manifest itself in the belief on the part of the man that his genitals have some defect. Nonsensical as this delusion is in most cases, it may lead to serious psychical derangements. Impotence is therefore one of the causes for sterility, though sterility is often associated with normal capacity for coitus. In cases of sterility, sexual functions are apparently normal, but the semen contains either no sperms or too few. Absence of sperms is scientifically known as azoospermia while insufficiency of sperms is called oligospermia. In most cases the cause is supposed to lie in an earlier inflammation of the epididimys of gonorrhoeal origion. This is, to say the least, unwarranted because, when the father, grandfather and great grandfather of the person concerned had never been guilty of moral lapses and they had never suffered from gonorrhoeal infection, how can the 'absence of sperm' in the person concerned have

gonorrhoeal origin? When science cannot explain things
with the aid of commonsense reasoning and ordinary
logic it resorts to unambiguous and unnatural causes.
On the other hand, we have specimens of normal persons
perfectly healthy but unable to beget children. This form
of masculine sterility is fairly frequent. Again the
medical man attributes feminine sterility to defects in her
genitals. We have been consulted by a number of persons
about their 5th bhava and several couples have confessed
before us that their sexual lives have been perfectly
normal. Therefore sterility in woman cannot be due to
sexual maladjustment on her part and the cause is something different. It has been estimated that at the present
time in the United States about one marriage in ten is
infertile. Lack of children in a family that wants them
is so serious a matter, yet it is unfortunate that so many
couples, disappointed year after year, make no effort to
discover the reason for their disappointment. Astrological
knowledge offers possibilities of investigation of the causes
of sterility.   Horoscopic examination can reveal the
conditions preventing a conception which may be
remedied. As we have said above, the medical man has a
ready but unproven explanation, *viz.*, a medical history
of gonorrhoea which explains a male's sterility.

The same gonorrhoea which is said to cause inflammation of the fallopian tubes or of the ovaries is supposed
to be the most frequent cause of sterility in the female
also. Fibroid tumours are another explanation of female
sterility. The doctor may no doubt say that although the
man or woman may be absoultely sterile so long as the
deleterious condition presists, treatment at the hands of a
skilled specialist may in many causes restore fertility. In
other words, everything depends upon the cause of the
trouble and the fun of it is the cause for fertility has so

far eluded the mental grasp of the medical man that it has developed upon the astrologer to explain the true cause and suggest the remedy.

Viewing things practically it may be said without fear of contradiction that sterility is often an impediment to marriage. Such cases present a considerable difficulty in that it is very frequently impossible to determine before marriage, by means of medical examination, whether a woman is capable of bearing children or not. Although absolute regularity and normality of the menstrual cycle may as a rule be taken as evidence in favour of fertility, there are many cases of sterility associated with such a menstrual cycle. Science does not and cannot know the essential criterion of feminine fertility so long as it refuses to absorb the knowledge offered by astrology. The bio-chemistry of fertility as a whole is still largely a closed book to science. The role of endocrine secretions in relation to fertility is equally obscure as yet. Science does not even know whether or not there is such a thing as normal sterility.

We have emphasised these obscurities for a definite reason. It happens frequently that in childless marriages, especially in Hindu Society where the birth of a son is of supreme importance, the fault is attributed by husband and relations alike to the wife alone, and sometimes she is accussed of having deliberately concealed her deficiency. It may be that the husband alone is responsible for sterility. In such cases, the astrological writers have suggested certain remedial measures.

There are several rules given in astrological books which enable us to find out the details pertaining to the 5th house intimately. Before the 5th house is examined, it is very essential to find out the sterility or otherwise of he marrying couple or even the husband and wife. Though

the fifth house may be strong and all the indications for
the birth or children be present, there will be no issues if
there is no strength or vitality for Beeja and Kshetra.
Beeja is the seed of the male and Kshetra is the bed of the
woman. In other words Beeja and Kshetra represent,
not exactly the sperm and the ovum, but the element that
really makes the male and female fluids fertile. The husband and wife may be physiologically normal. Their sex
relations may be happy. But still if the Beeja and the
Kshetra in their horoscopes are not strong, when judged
according to astrological rules, they will not bring forth
any issues. When the Beeja (male) is weak and Kshetra
(female) is strong, then children may be born late in life
after undertaking the necessary remedial measures. The
strength to cause pregnancy is contributed by the Sun—
lord of vitality—in general. The seminal fluid is governed
by Venus. These too must have favourable positions in
the horoscope particularly in odd signs. Similarly, in the
case of a female, Mars governs the nature of blood and the
Moon controls the strength to bear children. These two
planets should preferably occupy even signs. The following simple rule can be easily tested in the majority of
cases, unless other elusive combinations are present in the
horoscope.

In the case of a male, add together the longitude of
the Sun, Venus and Jupiter. Expunge multiples of 360°.
The sign arrived at indicates what is called 'Beejasputa' or
the longitude of the seed. Similarly in a female horoscope,
add together the longitudes of Mars, the Moon and Jupiter.
Expunge multiples of 360°. The sign arrived at represents
the longitude of the bed (Kshetra sphuta). If Beeja
sphuta occupies an odd sign and odd Navamsa and is
aspected by or associated with benefics, then there is
strength in the seed and the person is capable of procrea-

tion. Similarly the Kshetra sphuta should fall in an even sign and even Navamsa and should be associated with or aspected by benefics, in order to render the female fertile. Evil and impotent planets should not aspect these sensitive points, nor should evil planets occupy the 5th from Beeja and Kshetra sphutas. Kshetra or Beeja should not fall in a malefic sign even when it is friendly. Rahu should never join these two sensitive points.

Chart No. 88.—*Male born on 8-8-1912 at 7-35 p.m. (I.S.T.) (Lat. 13° N., Long. 5h. 10m. E.)*

Rahu	Saturn Moon			Saturn	Venus
Lagna	RASI		Sun (Beeja)	Sun Rahu	AMSA	
			Mars Venus Merc.	Lagna		Merc. Moon Ketu (Beeja)
	Jupiter		Ketu		Jupiter	Mars

Balance of Mars Dasa at birth :   Years 6–1–6.

Beeja Sphuta

		Degrees	Minutes
Sun's Longitudes	...	112	43
Venus' ,,	...	121	48
Jupiter's ,,	...	221	11
		455	42

Expunging 360° the remainder is 95° 42′ which locates *Beeja* in Cancer in Rasi and Leo in Navamsa. *Beeja* though an even sign in Rasi is occupied by lord of vitality, *viz.*, the Sun and the Beeja has not only fallen in a benefic sign but is aspected by Jupiter and Saturn. The 5th from Beeja is occupied by Jupiter. In the Navamsa. the Beeja occupies an odd Rasi and the 5th is free from evil planets. These indicate the strength of the Beeja.

Chart No. 89.—*Female born on 16-10-1918 at 2-20 p.m. (I.S.T.) (Lat. 13° N., Long. 5h. 10m. 20s. E.)*

	Ketu	Jupit.		Jupiter Saturn
Moon	No. 2 WIFE RASI		Rahu	Venus
			AMSA	
Lagna		Sat.	Moon	Ketu
Kshetra	Mars Rahu	Sun Mercury	Venus	Mars	Kshetra	Sun Mercury	Lagna

Balance of Rahu Dasa at birth :   Years 11–8–20.

Kshetra Sphuta

		Degrees	Minutes
Longitude of Jupiter	...	83	35
,, Mars	...	229	49
,, Moon	...	311	43
		625	07

Expunging 360°, the remainder is 265° 07′ which locates the Kshetra in Sagittarius 25° 7′. In Rasi, Kshetra occupies a benefic sign (though odd) aspected by Jupiter. In the Navamsa, the Kshetra is in (Scorpio) an even sign aspected by Jupiter and Saturn. Thus the Kshethra is fertile indicating the birth of children. In both the cases above referred to, owing to the fact that Beeja is an even sign (in Rasi in the male horoscope) and Kshetra is in odd sign (in Rasi in the female horoscope) the fertility cannot be in a pronounced manner. Hence the number of children cannot be very large. The natives of the above two horoscopes are no doubt healthy but have weak constitutions appropriate with saturnine influences on Lagna but the children have been perfectly healthy.

The native of the following horoscope is quite hale and healthy. With all searching medical examination, no constitutional defects have been found. Doctors have said that the powers of procreation are perfectly normal, yet he has no children.

Chart No. 90.—*Details of Birth withheld for obvious reasons.*

	Moon Venus	Sun Mercury	Ketu		Mars	Mercury	Rahu
		No. 3 RASI		Sat.		AMSA	Sun Lagna
(Beeja)			Lagna Mars	Jupit. (Beeja)			Moon
Rahu	Saturn	Jupiter		Ketu	Venus		

Leaving aside the 5th bhava, find out the Beeja disposition.

		Degrees
Sun's Longitude	...	53
Jupiter's ,,	..	192
Venus' ,,	...	26
		271 = Capricorn 1°

The Beeja has fallen in an even and malefic sign both in Rasi and Amsa. In Rasi, .the Beeja is aspected by Saturn while in Amsa Jupiter is neecha in Beejasthana.

All these indicate sterlity. Several other rules are to be found for determining sterility or otherwise of a person concerned and certain rules have to be applied only under certain planetary combinations. If the Beeja or Kshetra longitude has a larger number of malefic saptavargas, fertility is completely absent. The remedies for sterility will be discussed on a subsequent occasion. Thus most of these anomalies can be discovered or determined by astrological examination of the horoscope of the couple before marriage ; and a fairly definite if not a truly correct prognosis as to capacity to produce or bear children can be made in a good number of cases.

The Fifth House.—The 5th house in Chart No. 91 is Libra a movable sign and is occupied by the malefics Sun and Mercury and aspected by the malefic Saturn, lord of the 8th.

The Fifth Lord.—The 5th lord Venus is debilitated occupying the 12th or house of loss from the 5th and associated with Rahu a first-rate malefic and is in a kendra from Mars.

Putrakaraka.—Jupiter, the karaka for children, is no doubt in the 9th with the Moon but as he is subject to Papakarthari Yoga and occupies a malefic Rasi, he is also blemished.

15

Chart No. 91.—*Born on 30–10–1903 at 9–30 p.m. (L.M.T.) (Lat. 17° 40' N., Long. 75° 57' E.)*

Ketu		Lagna		Mandi Jupiter	Mars Rahu
Moon Jupit.	RASI		Sun	AMSA	Sat.
Sat.		Mandi	Lagna Moon Venus		
Mars	Sun Mercury	Rahu Venus		Ketu	Mercury

Balance of Rahu Dasa at birth : Years 12–11–24.

Conclusion.—All the three factors *viz.*, the house, the lord and the karaka are considerably afflicted. From Chandra Lagna again the 5th is aspected by Mars while the 5th lord is blemished in exactly the same way as the 5th house from Lagna. Hence the native has had no issues born to him, even though married to 4 wives. Readers may also examine the strength of Beeja in this horoscope by applying the principles given on page 72.

The Fifth House.—The 5th house in Chart No. 92 is Gemini, a common sign, and is unafflicted either by aspect or association.

The Fifth Lord.—Mercury the lord is no doubt exalted but he is considerably afflicted by association with three malefics, *viz.*, the Sun, Mars and Ketu.

Putrakaraka.—The karaka, Jupiter, is in Scorpio, a malefic sign aspected by Saturn.

Conclusion.—While the karaka and the house are moderately blemished, the lord is considerably afflicted.

Chart No. 92.—*Born on 30–9–1912 at 5–15 p.m. (I.S.T.) (Lat. 30° 19' N., Long. 75° 25' E.)*

Rahu		Saturn Moon			Saturn Mereury	Snu
Lagna		RASI			AMSA	Ketu
				Lagna Moon Rahu Mandi		
	Jupiter	Venus Mandi	Sun Mars Merc. Ketu	Jupit. Venus		Mars

Balance of Sun Dasa at birth : Years 3–1–16.

From Chandra Lagna, the 5th house and the 5th lord are subject to a number of afflictions. Consequently the native did not have any issue. He died before the completion of Rahu Dasa. If the native had good longevity, perhaps he would got an issue in Jupiter Dasa.

The Fifth House.—In Chart No. 93 Aries, the fifth house, is aspected by Mars the 5th lord. Otherwise the house has no aspect or association.

The Fifth Lord.—Mars the 5th lord is considerably afflicted by his association with Rahu and 8th lord Moon. No benefic aspects the lord. In the Navamsa also Mars is aspected by Saturn.

Putrakaraka.—Jupiter is subjected to Papakarthari Yoga. Otherwise he is well placed.

Conclusion.—The horoscope is peculiarly disposed so far as the fifth (children) and seventh (wife) bhavas are concerned. Mark the fact that Mercury lord of the 7th is

Chart No. 93.—*Born on 3-6-1903 at 4-45 p.m.*
(L.M.T.) (Lat. 11° 6' N., Long. 79° 44' E.)

Ketu	Sun Mercury		Mandi Mars			Jupit. Sat.
Jupit.		Venus	Moon			Sun Rahu Merc.
Sat. Mandi	RASI		Ketu		AMSA	
Lagna		Mars Rahu Moon		Venus	Lagna	

Balance of Sun Dasa at birth : Years 2–5–29.

in the 12th (from 7th) with malefic Sun. From Chandra
Lagna the 5th house is occupied by Saturn the lord, while
in the Navamsa the fifth from Chandra is strongly afflicted
by the presence of Putrakaraka and Saturn further aspected
by Mars. The native's wife has separated and he has no
children born to him.

The Fifth House.—The 5th house, in Chart No. 94
Cancer in this case, is powerfully afflicted owing to the
presence of three first-rate malefics, *viz.,* the Sun, Saturn
and Rahu. Jupiter's aspect and the presence of Venus, do
not counterbalance the evil due to the location of three
malefic planets.

The Fifth Lord.—The 5th lord Moon is equally
afflicted by his conjunction with Mars, in the 8th.

Putrakaraka.—Jupiter is fairly well disposed as he is
in a trikona from the 5th house.

Conclusion.—As both the 5th lord and the 5th house
are considerably afflicted, the native has had no issues.

Chart No. 94.—*Born on 16-7-1888 at 11-6 p.m. (L.M.T.) (Lat. 18° 54' N., Long. 72° 49' E.)*

			Merc.	Ketu	Mercury	
Lagna						
Mandi			Sun Venus Rahu Sat.	Lagna	AMSA	
	RASI					Sun Jupit. Venus
Ketu						
	Jupiter	Mars Moon		Moon Sat. Mandi	Mars	Rahu

Balance of Rahu Dasa at birth : Years 17-5-24.

Mark also the affliction of the 5th lord from Chandra Lagna and of the 5th house from Navamsa Lagna. Any tyro in astrology, who looks at this horoscope, can say that the 5th house is unfortunately disposed for progeny.

The Fifth House.—Libra is the 5th house in Chart No. 95 and it is not occupied by any planet. Mars and Jupiter aspect the 5th house, the former's aspect being bad and that of the latter being good.

The Fifth Lord.—The lord Venus is in Lagna with Mercury and is aspected by Jupiter. Against this benefic disposition is the Papakarthari Yoga to which Venus is subjected.

Putrakaraka.—Jupiter, the karaka, is no doubt in the 9th but his association with Rahu and the combined aspects of Mars and Saturn he receives, have rendered him highly malefic.

Conclusion.—The 5th house and the 5th lord are rendered neutral by the almost equal distribution of benefic

Chart No. 95.—*Born on 2-6-1914 at 7-5 a.m. (I.S.T.) (Lat. 22° 45' N., Long. 72° 41' E.)*

		Sun Saturn	Lagna Venus Merc.	Venus Rahu Mandi			Sun
Jupit. Rahu			Mars	Mars			
	RASI		— —		AMSA		
			Moon Ketu				
			Mandi	Merc.	Lagna Moon	Jupiter	Sat. Ketu

Balance of Venus Dasa at birth :   Years 1–4–24.

and malefic influences.   Putrakaraka Jupiter is capable of producing the most baneful effects.   Mark the fact that Jupiter also happens to be the lord of the 5th house from Chandra Lagna.

Though it is 30 years since he married, the native has had no issues born to him.

The Fifth House.—The 5th house in Chart No. 96 is Kumbha or Aquarius, a fixed sign, and is occupied by Mars, a first-rate malefic.   This is a bad disposition.   The 5th is further aspected by Saturn, another first-rate malefic thus augmenting the evil considerably.

The Fifth Lord.—The 5th lord Saturn is no doubt in a benefic sign, aspecting the 5th house.   But Saturn is aspected by Mars, so that the mutual aspects between Saturn and Mars involving the 5th house are capable of destroying the 5th house indications.

Chart No. 96.—*Born on 28-3-1913 at 8-35 p.m. (I.S.T.) (Lat. 29° N., Long. 72° 40' E.)*

Sun Rahu Merc.	Venus	Saturn		Sat.	Ketu	Moon	
Mars							
	RASI				AMSA		
			Lagna				
Moon Mandi Jupit.	Lagna	Ketu		Mars	Sun Mercury Jupiter	Venus Rahu	Mandi

Balance of Ketu Dasa at birth :   Years 4-0-22.

Putrakaraka.—Jupiter, the karaka, is in his own house with the Moon otherwise unafflicted.

Conclusion.—Since the house and the lord are considerably afflicted, the karaka's moderately benefic disposition should be ignored. The native, though married in 1930, has had no issues. Mark also the affliction of the 5th lord from Chandra Lagna.

The Fifth House.—In Chart No. 97. the 5th is Kumbha. Rahu's presence there, and Putrakaraka being hemmed in between malefics are unfortunate combinations. The 5th is not aspected by any benefics or malefics.

The Fifth Lord.—Saturn the 5th lord is in Gemini aspected by malefics the Sun, Mars and Mercury. The 5th lord is therefore subjected to considerable affliction.

Putrakaraka.—Jupiter, Putrakaraka, has all the evil influences, to which the 5th house is subject, focussed on him.

Chart No. 97.—*Born on 25/24–12–1914 at 2–30 a.m. (I.S.T.) (Lat. 22° 43' N., Long. 71° 43' E.)*

Moon		Sat.		Mercury Mandi	Ketu
Rahu	RASI		AMSA		Sun Mars
Jupit.		Ketu			Venus
Sun Mars Merc.	Venus	Lagna Mandi	Lagna Moon Sat. Rahu		Jupit.

Balance of Mercury Dasa at birth : Years 16–9–29.

Conclusion.—As all the three factors, *viz.*, the house, the lord and the karaka are considerably afflicted, the 5th house is spoilt. The native has not so far got any issue though he married nearly 30 years ago.

The Fifth House.—In Chart No. 98, the 5th is Capricorn a movable sign and is not afflicted either by association or aspect. From Chandra Lagna however the 5th, being occupied by Saturn and Putrakaraka, is not a desirable feature.

The Fifth Lord.—Saturn the 5th lord occupying the 12th from the 5th has rendered the 5th house weak from Chandra Lagna. The 5th lord, in association with Saturn, though in his own house, has weakened the lord.

Putrakaraka.— Jupiter, the karaka, occupies the 12th from the 5th (from Lagna) and the 5th from Chandra Lagna. He is in association with malefic Saturn. Jupiter is therefore rendered feebly weak.

Chart No. 98.—*Born on 24–5–1901 at 1–36 p.m.
(L.M.T.) (Lat. 17° 0′ N., Long. 81° 50′ E.)*

		Ketu Sun Venus Mercury Mandi		Sun Moon		Venus
			Lagna	AMSA		Rahu Merc. Mandi
	RASI					
		Moon Mars	Ketu			Mars
Sat. Jupit.	Rahu	Lagna		Saturn	Jupiter	

Balance of Ketu Dasa at birth : Years 6–5–27.

Conclusion.—In view of afflictions to which the lord and the karaka are subject to the 5th bhava is rendered weak with the result no children have been born to him either by the first or the second wife.

The Fifth House.—In Chart No. 99, the 5th house, a fixed sign, is subjected to Papakarthari Yoga. It is aspected by two benefics, *viz.*, Jupiter and Venus, and a first-rate malefic Saturn.

The Fifth Lord.—Mars the 5th lord is in the 6th from Lagna in a benefic sign otherwise unafflicted. His being in a kendra from Saturn is not desirable.

Putrakaraka.—Jupiter, the karaka is in his own sign, aspecting the 5th house and aspected by Mars and Saturn.

Conclusion.—In interpreting combinations, due consideration should be given to the dual roles played by the involved planets, as natural benefics or malefics and as benefic or malefic lords. For instance, Jupiter is a natural

Chart No. 99.—*Born on 12-4-1892 at 12-45 p.m. (L.M.T.) (Lat. 11° 36' N., Long. 71° 5' E.)*

Jupit.	Sun Mercury Rahu	Venus	
			Lagna *Mandi*
	RASI		Sat.
Mars		Moon Ketu	Sat.

Sun	Venus	Ketu
		Merc.
AMSA		*Mandi*
Mars Rahu	Jupiter	Lagna Moon

Balance of Mars Dasa at birth : Years 2–3–2.

benefic. He may become a malefic lord by virtue of ownership of certain houses (*vide* page 17 of 1 part of HOW TO JUDGE A HOROSCOPE). In interpreting a combination involving Jupiter, the astrologer must be able to balance the benefic effects due to Jupiter being a natural benefic and the unfavourable result he gives as a malefic lord.

The disposition of 5th house and the 5th lord indicates the birth of children. But as Putrakaraka has the combined influences of two first-rate malefics, Mars, ruling the 5th house here and the karaka for blood, and Saturn, the karaka for sorrow aspecting the 5th, the native has to experience sorrow on account of the 5th house. The sign from which Mars aspects the 5th house is a fiery one. The native's wife had 4 or 5 abortions and no fully developed children were born.

Chart No. 100.—*Born on 3/2–6–1897 at 5–30 a.m. (L.M.T.) (Lat. 16° 8' N., Long. 80° 41' E.)*

	Venus	Lagna Sun Mercury	Moon		Moon	Mandi		Rahu
			Mars Ketu		Merc.			Lagna Sun Jupit. Venus
	RASI				AMSA			
Rahu			Jupit.					Sat.
Mandi	Saturn				Mars Ketu			

Balance of Rahu Dasa at birth : Years 0–11–26.

The Fifth House.—Virgo happens to be the 5th house. It is free from affliction. From Chandra Lagna the 5th house happens to be Libra and it is aspected by Mars. In the Navamsa the 5th house is aspected by Jupiter. Hence the 5th house is nominally or feebly strong.

The Fifth Lord.—The 5th lord Mercury is in Lagna with a malefic Sun and aspected by another malefic Saturn and hence afflicted. From Chandra Lagna, the 5th lord Venus aspects the 5th and Venus in his turn is aspected by Jupiter. In the Navamsa the 5th lord is Mars and he is with Ketu in Sagittarius. Hence the 5th lord is weak.

Putrakaraka.—Jupiter, Putrakaraka, occupying a malefic sign, is aspected by Saturn from another malefic sign Scorpio. In the Navamsa Jupiter is no doubt exalted but his association with the Sun and his being aspected by Mars are not good features.

Conclusion.—The 5th house is feebly strong, the lord
is weak and the karaka powerless. Birth of children is
not altogether ruled out.   But the 5th house indications
are a source of misery for the native. One male issue
was born in 1922 and died immediately. Subsequently
there were two abortions.

   Chart No. 101.—*Born on 6-5-1891 at 5-10 p.m.
(L.M.T.) (Lat. 18° 54' N., Long. 72° 49' E.)*

Venus	Sun Moon	Mars Rahu Mercury			Moon Jupiter	Rahu
Jupit.						Mars
	RASI				AMSA	
			Sat.	Merc.		
	Ketu	Lagna		Lagna Venus	Sun Ketu	Sat.

   Balance of Ketu Dasa at birth : Year 6-3-12.

   The Fifth House.—The 5th house is Aquarius and it
is occupied by Jupiter Putrakaraka and hence bad. The
5th is aspected by Saturn the 5th lord. This is good. The
5th from Chandra Lagna is occupied by the malefic Saturn
and aspected by another malefic Mars. Hence the 5th
house is strongly blemished.

   The Fifth Lord.—The fifth lord Saturn is in the house
of an enemy but aspected by Jupiter and Mars. Hence he
is neither good nor bad.

   Putrakaraka.—Jupiter is Putrakaraka in the fifth
house is not a good position. His being aspected by

Saturn (ignoring the fact that Saturn is lord of the 5th) is not desirable.

Conclusion. – As lord of the 5th house aspecting the 5th and Putrakaraka, birth of issue is denoted. But as the 5th house is afflicted and the 5th lord almost weak, their survival is not shown. The native's wife had five abortions and one was still-born. One fully developed child was born on 1-6-1937 but died on 13-4-1938. No surviving issues now.

Chart No. 102.—*Born on 29-12-1880 at 10-10 a.m. (L.M.T.) (Lat. 22° 35' N., Long. 88° 23' E.)*

Jupit. Mandi	Saturn		Ketu	Mars	Saturn Mercury	Rahu	
Lagna				Lagna			
	RASI				AMSA		
Venus							
Sun Merc. Rahu	Mars Moon			Jupit.	Ketu Moon	Mandi	Sun Venus

Balance of Saturn Dasa at birth : Years 4-7-9.

The Fifth House.—The 5th house, *viz.,* Gemini, is occupied by Ketu and aspected by malefics Sun, Mars and Mercury. Hence the 5th is considerably afflicted. From Chandra Lagna the 5th is occupied by Jupiter, who is not only Putrakaraka but lord of the 5th from the Moon.

The Fifth Lord.—The fifth lord Mercury is afflicted by his association with malefics Sun and Rahu. In the

Navamsa also Mercury is strongly blemished by association with Saturn and being subjected to Papakartari
Yoga.

Putrakaraka.—Whilst his position in his own house is
good, his being in the 5th from Chandra Lagna, as Putrakaraka, is harmful.

Conclusion.—The 5th house is spoilt and is a source
of worry to the native. A male child was born on
15–10–1898 and died within one month. Subsequently no
otheir issues were born.

We shall now illustrate a few charts for the birth of
only one issue and for the birth of several issues. The
reader must study all the combinations bearing on the 5th
house carefully and apply the appropriate ones. There
are thousands of combinations given in standard astrological works and it would be impossible to catalogue them
in a book of this type. Besides the ordinary combinations,
there are special yogas pertaining to children and some of
these yogas have been enumerated in my book THREE
HUNDRED IMPORTANT COMBINATIONS. Readers may
profitably refer to this book also. The art of judging a
house can be divided into two parts, analysis and synthesis.
In the former process, the combinations, bearing on a
bhava or event, are split up to ascertain the exact influence of each conjuction and aspect, while in the latter,
the isolated pieces of information are built up into one
co-ordinated whole.

In Chart No. 103, Ketu is in the 5th house aspected
by Mars. This combination, in the absence of any relief
from beneficial sources, is formidable enough to adversely
affect the house of children. However as 5th lord Saturn
is aspected by Jupiter and Putrakaraka Jupiter is himself
free from affliction, birth of children is not denied. From

Chart No. 103.—*Born on 5/6–12–1906 at 1–10 a.m. (I.S.T.) (Lat. 10° 44' N., Long. 79° 6' E.)*

	Mandi	Jupit.	Jupit. Sat.		Mandi Ketu
Sat.		Moon Rahu	Lagna	AMSA	
Ketu	RASI		Sun		
Sun Mercury Venus	Mars	Lagna		Moon Rahu	Mars Venus	Merc.

Balance of Saturn Dasa at birth : Years 3–1–19.

Chandra Lagna, the 5th has less benefic and more malefic forces concentrated on it by virtue of the situation of Venus, Sun and Mercury therein and the aspect of Saturn. Only one daughter was born just at the beginning of Ketu Dasa and she is living. That apart the native has had no issues.

The native has only one daughter. Mark, while the 5th house is fairly well disposed, the 5th lord Saturn and Putrakaraka are both considerably afflicted, the former being associated with three malefics Sun, Mercury and Moon and aspected by Mars and the latter being aspected by Mars. From Chandra Lagna, the situation of Rahu in the 5th being aspected by Mars suggests some miscarriages and premature births.

Innumerable rules have been given in ancient works to ascertain the number of issues, and losses and survivals among them. I do not propose to expand these in the

Chart No. 104.—*Born on 11-4-1907 at 6-50 p.m. (I.S.T.) (Lat. 11° 15' N., Long. 75° 45' E.)*

Sun Moon Merc. Sat.			Jupit.	Sun Ketu	Venus		Merc. Sat.
Venus Mandi			Rahu				
	RASI				AMSA		M
Ketu			Jupit.				
Mars		Lagna			Mandi Moon	Lagna	Rahu

Balance of Saturn Dasa at birth : Years 3–2–6.

pages of this book. I shall give a few typical illustrations and the intelligent reader can study such charts in the light of principles which may be gathered from any standard astrological works. Usually the number of children to be born is guessed by the number of Navamsas gained by the 5th house or 5th lord. If the 5th lord is aspected by Jupiter or Venus, the number is doubled. Malefics occupying the intervening Navamsas denote possible losses.

In Chart No. 105, the 5th house is unafflicted as no benefic or malefic occupies or aspects it. From Chandra Lagna, however, both Mars and Jupiter aspect the 5th house. The 5th lord Venus is with the Sun and Mercury, while Jupiter Putrakaraka, having caused Gajakesari, is aspected by Mars. Rahu and Ketu have nothing to do with the 5th house. Consequently the 5th house is fairly well disposed. The 5th lord Venus has gained by 5

Chart No. 105.—*Born on 6-1-1906 at 5-24 p.m. (I.S.T.) (Lat. 30° N., Long. 78° E.)*

		Moon Jupiter	Lagna	Mars	Rahu Mercury	Lagna
Mars Sat. Ketu				Mandi Moon Jupit.		
	RASI				AMSA	
Mandi			Rahu			Venus
Sun Merc. Venus				Sat.	Sun	Ketu

Balance of Sun Dasa at birth : Years 1–7–21.

Navamsa indicating 5 issues. In the Navamsa he is aspected by the Moon and Jupiter. Hence doubling the number, we have 10. As Rahu intervenes between Aries the 1st Navamsa) and Venus, the number of children) may be put at about 9. The native had 8 issues out of which one died.

The 5th house in Chart No. 106 is highly significant. From Lagna the 5th is aspected by Mars Lagnadhipathi and by the Moon. The aspect of Mars a natural malefic is bad but as Lagnadhipathi it is good. The Moon's aspect produces beneficial influence favouring the birth of more of female children. The fifth lord Sun is with Mars in a benefic (though inimical) sign and is aspected by Jupiter who has obtained neechabhanga. Putrakaraka Jupiter is neechabhanga but has joined Saturn. The combinations are indicative of birth as well as loss of

16

Chart No. 106.— *Born on 30/29–5–1902 at 3–19 a.m. (L.T.) (Lat. 17° N., Long. 81° 46' E.)*

	Ketu Lagna Venus Madni	Sun Mars	Merc.		Mandi	Sun Venus	
Moon				Sat.			Lagna Ketu
Jupit. Sat.	RASI			Mars Rahu	AMSA		Jupit.
		Rahu		Moon Merc.			

Balance of Rahu Dasa at birth : Years 14–1–1.

children. From Chandra Lagna, the 5th house is well
fortified by the presence of Mercury, the 5th lord. The
5th lord Sun has gained 5 Navamsas. He is in Vargottama.
Besides this, the mid-point of the 5th bhava falls in the
same Navamsa. Consequently trebling the number of
Navamsa gained by the Sun, we have 15, the probable
number of children to be born.   Actually so far 13
children have been born out of which, due to affliction
of the 5th lord and Putrakaraka by Mars and Saturn
respectively, the native has lost 3 issues.

Chart No. 107 is peculiar in the sense that the native
has no sons but only daughters. The 5th from Lagna is
an even sign occupied by a hermaphrodite planet Mercury
and subject to Papakarthari Yoga. The 5th lord is, of
course, Mars. The 5th from Chandra Lagna is an even
and feminine sign and the lord happens to be a hermaphrodite planet. The 5th is aspected by the feminine
planet Saturn. The exaltation of Putrakaraka and the

Chart No. 107.—*Born on 24/23-10-1907 at 2 a.m. (I.S.T.) (Lat. 23° 2' N., Long. 72° 19' E.)*

Sat.	Moon	Rahu	**RASI**
Mars		Lagna Jupit.	
Ketu	Mercury	Sun Venus	

Moon Venus		Mars	Rahu
	AMSA		Merc. Sat.
Jupit.			
Lagna Sun Ketu			

Balance of the Sun Dasa at birth : Year 1-0-7.
lord of 5th house renders the 5th house sound while the predominance of the feminine elements in the 5th from Lagna and from Chandra Lagna indicates the birth of female children. Mars has gained five Navamsas. Mars is in a benefic Navamsa and aspected by the benefic Jupiter.

Here is another typical case (Chart No. 108) of the birth of a number of children and the loss of all but one. Putrakaraka in the 5th house aspected by Mars and the 5th house from the Moon being occupied by Saturn—Ketu association is a clear case of the spoiling of the 5th house. As Mars is lord of the 5th and aspects the 5th, there is affliction on account of the birth and death of children. Mars, the 5th lord, has gained 5 Navamsas. Since Mars is in the 11th from Putrakaraka in Navamsa and otherwise unafflicted, the total number of children is shown to be about 10. In fact 10 children were born, out of which only one daughter survives.

Chart No. 108 — *Born on 29/28–1–1905 at 5 a.m. (I.S.T.) (Lat. 9° 43' N., Long. 76° 13' E.)*

Venus	Jupiter		Ketu	Jupiter	Sun Moon
Ketu Sat.	RASI		Mars	AMSA	Venus
Sun		Rahu			
Lagna Merc.	Moon Mars		Mercury	Saturn	Lagna Rahu

Balance of Jupiter Dasa at birth : Years 4–4–24.

The examples given above are adequate to convince the reader that much skill is required in judging children from a horoscope. It is very necessary that the horoscopes of both the husband and the wife are examined in order to get a correct picture about the birth of off-spring. It often happens that the 5th house afflicted in the case of the husband is made good by a favourable disposition in the case of the wife and *vice versa*. The nature of the Lagna and the sign falling in the 5th and the nature of the planets occupying or aspecting the 5th indicate the size of the family. The sex of the children should be judged by the signs and planets and the special yogas involving the 5th house. The horoscopes have to be examined carefully and the indications balanced cleverly. Intelligently and scientifically applied, the results derived will be quite satisfactory. This book gives the hints. The rest is in the hands of the clever reader.

9. Concerning the Sixth House

The sixth house rules or signifies accidents, diseases, enemies, mental affliction, mother's brother and misfortunes. An affliction to the sixth house may result in the shape of the person suffering diseases or incurring debts or enemies. In reality however a person may be suffering from diseases, but be free from debts or he may be perfectly healthy but involved in huge debts. The difficulty arises in differentiating the different events comprehended by a single house. If one rushes headlong into making predictions without a thorough study of the theory and without gaining adequate practical experience, he will draw quite wrong conclusions.

Main Considerations

In analysing the sixth bhava, one has to carefully study the strength of (a) the Bhava, (b) the Karaka, (c) the Lord, and (d) Occupants. Planets involved in aspecting the house and the lord are also important. Several arishta yogas having a bearing on the sixth house should be carefully studied.

Results of Lord of Sixth House Occupying Different Houses

In the first House.—Well aspected, the person may join the army as a soldier or Commander consistent with the strength or otherwise of the disposition. Or he may become a Minister of War or an official or officer concerned with prisons. He will live in the house of his maternal uncle. If the sixth lord is weak and otherwise afflicted, he will become a robber or a thief or leader of a criminal gang.

In the Second House.—Conjoined with or aspected by benefics the native will have untold suffering in family life and deep sorrows, loss of money through enemies, defective vision, uneven teeth and stammer .. the sixth lord is weak and otherwise ill-disposed in the 2nd, there will be loss of wife in the Dasa or Bhukti of the malefic lord. If Venus is weak, the native will be a celibate and poverty stricken, just able to get a morsel of food when hungry.

In the Third House.—The sixth lord fortified confers enmity with brothers. Or his maternal uncle befriending the native's brother works against the native's interests or the native's brother suffers from frequent ill-health. The 6th lord weak and afflicted, the native will have no younger brothers.

In the Fourth House.—Well fortified, lives in a dilapidated building. He will have breaks in education and will discard his mother. Maternal uncles will generally be land cultivators. Weak and afflicted : he will quarrel with his mother and ancestral property will be involved in debts. He will work as a menial and lead a miserable life. Troublesome home and domestic affairs and trouble through servants.

In the Fifth House.—Sickly children. The native will be adopted by his maternal uncle and become fortunate.

In the Sixth House.—Increase of cousins. Native's maternal uncle becomes famed. If in conjunction with weak Lagnadhipathi, he will suffer from an incurable disease and increase of enmity with kith and kin.

In the Seventh House.—Generally marries mother's, brother's or father's sister's daughter. The maternal uncle lives in a far-off place (or a foreign country). The wife's character will be doubtful. If the sixth lord is afflicted, he will either divorce his wife early in life or she will die. If the Rasi and Navamsa involved are hermaphrodite ones, he will have a sickly or barren wife. When Lagnadhipati joins the sixth lord in the 7th which happens to be a hermaphrodite sign, the native will be a eunuch and unable to perform the sexual act. There will also be troubles with disrespectable women.

In the Eighth House.—When fortified, he will have Madhyayu or middle life. When afflicted, he will have plenty of debts and will suffer from loathsome diseases. He will hunt after women other than his own wife and take pleasure in inflicting pain on others.

In the Ninth House.—Father becomes a judge, if the sixth lord is well fortified. The maternal uncle becomes highly fortunate. There will be misunderstandings between him and his father. There will be benefits from *Gnatis* or cousins. If afflicted : poverty, sinful acts, misfortunes through relatives, ungrateful towards preceptors and engaged in unrighteous deeds. If moderate : becomes a mason, timber merchant or stone cutter.

In the Tenth House.—If fortified : Sinful and destructive nature, poses as an orthodox and pious man but really unscrupulous in regard to religious matters. When the lord is weak : dismissal formidable enemies, low life or begging.

In the Eleventh House.—If benefic, eldest brother will be a judge. If ordinary : an elder brother becomes a judge for some time but loses his job. If malefic : poor and wretched life ; suffering on account of convictions.

In the Twelfth House.—Well disposed : difficulty and sorrow through destructive nature ; causes harm to others. If afflicted : miserable, hard and wretched existence.

The above are the general results likely to happen when the sixth lord is posited in the different bhavas. In applying them to actual charts, much care is needed. Unless the modifications due to benefic and malefic associations, aspects, etc., are borne in mind, it will be difficult to use these indications successfully.

Important Combinations

We shall now give some important combinations pertaining to the 6th house, selected from authoritative text-books.

If evil planets aspect or occupy the 6th, the native will have few enemies. If good planets aspect or occupy it, the number of enemies will increase. If the evil lord of the 6th resides in Lagna, 8th or 10th, he will suffer from boils. If the 6th lord is in the 6th or 8th with the Sun, he will suffer from boils in the head; with the Moon, in the face; with Mars or Mercury, in the front; with Jupiter, in the nose; with Venus, in the eyes; with Saturn, Rahu or Ketu, in the armpits. Lords of the 6th and 8th occupying the 7th and the 8th respectively will cause piles. The Sun, the Moon, Mars, Mercury, Jupiter, Venus or Saturn joining the lord of the 6th in the ascendant indicate respectively danger from high fevers, watery diseases or grandular swellings or ulcer, bilious complaints, consumption, sexual troubles, nervous diseases, carbuncle or spleen trouble. Evil planets in the 6th or lord of the 6th with Saturn or Rahu will cause the native to suffer always. One suffers greatly from fever in his 6th and 12th years if Mars is in the 6th and the lord of the 6th is in the 8th. He will contact leprosy in his 20th year if the Moon and Jupiter are in the 6th; watery diseases in 26th year if Rahu is in the 6th, and lord of Lagna is in the 8th; colic in the 30th year if there is Parivarthana (mutual exchange

(........ses) between lords of the 6th and the 12th ; rheumatic affections if the lord of Lagna is in Lagna with
lord of the 8th. There will be fear from wild animals if
Saturn is in the 6th house with the lord of the 8th and
lord of the 12th is in Lagna. One will be endangered
through w..er in the 5th or 9th year if the Sun is in the
6th or 8th and the Moon is in the 12th from the Sun.
Parivarthana between lords of the 6th and 12th denote
loss of money in the 31st or 40th year. The Sun
becomes an enemy if the 6th lord is in the 6th
with Jupiter and the 12th lord is in Lagna. The Moon
in the 6th with Mars indicates jaundiced constitution.
Saturn or Mars in the 6th aspected by Rahu or the Sun,
and the ascendant lord weak denotes lingering disease.
Heart or lung diseases are indicated if Saturn with Mandi
occupies the 6th and receives the aspect of the Sun, Mars
or Rahu.

If the lord of Lagna and the 6th join a kendra with
Saturn, the person will be confined : if with Rahu or Ketu,
he will be placed in irons. One will have a tragic end if
the Moon aspected by Lagnadhipathi joins Saturn, Rahu
or Ketu in the 6th, 8th or 12th. One will die in battle if the
lord of the 6th or 8th or Mars joins the 3rd lord with
Saturn and Rahu in cruel Navamsa. Parivarthana or
mutual aspects between Mars and the Sun, in Rasi or in
Navamsa, indicates death in a dual fight.

If the lord of the 6th is in a kendra aspected by evil
planets or many evil planets are in the 6th, the person
will be vexed by enemies. If the 6th lord is in the house
of a benefic planet and aspected by good planets, he will
have many friends. When lord of Lagna is in the 6th
aspected by lord of the 6th or if they both remain in
Lagna or in the 4th, the person will be constantly troubled
and vexed by his relatives. He will be put to difficulties
by relatives if Jupiter or Venus is in Lagna with lord of

the 6th aspected by Saturn, Rahu or Mars. He will suffer from thieves and fire if the 9th lord occupies the 6th, aspected by the 6th lord : if the 6th lord in the 6th is with Mars aspected by Rahu or Ketu, he will lose his estates by auction.

Planets in the Sixth House

The Sun.—The person becomes a good politician, famous and successful. Not very good for health. Sun afflicted : Long and troublesome illness. Sun fortified : Good administrative ability, few enemies, wealthy and generally successful in all endeavours. Affliction by Saturn is not desirable as it indicates heart-trouble or frequent chest pain unless the affliction is relieved by Jupiter's aspect.

The Moon.—Indicates Balarishta or much ill-health during early childhood. Affliction by Mars and Saturn : curious and incurable diseases and revengeful enemies. Moon strongly denotes ability and success in subordinate positions. If the sixth is a fixed sign, the person will suffer from stone in the bladder ; he will be submissive to women ; weak sexual connection and stomach troubles. Afflicted in common signs, danger from lung troubles. He will have success as a caterer.

Mars.—Highly passionate, victorious and successful as a ruler or politician. He will have worries from near relatives. Mars afflicted : accidents, losses and troubles through employees. If Saturn is the afflicting planet, death may be due to operation or injury by animals. If Rahu afflicts Mars, death may be due to suicide. If Ketu, he will die by poisoning.

Mercury.—Quarrelsome and showy but yet respected ; interrupted education. If afflicted, mental troubles and danger of nervous breakdown. If afflicted by Mars and

Rahu or Saturn and Rahu, there is danger of insanity through excitement, troubles with servants and a tendency to poor health. The person will be lazy, harsh in speech, but nevertheless, a terror to his enemies.

Jupiter.—Inactive, suffers disrespect, indulges in black magic, feared by enemies, unlucky, dyspeptic, health generally good. If afflicted, health suffers through over-indulgence.

Venus.—No enemies, corrupted by young women, favourable for getting favours from women. If afflicted : health affected by too much sexual indulgence, fond of other women and licentious.

Saturn.—Quarrelsome, obstinate, voracious eater, foeless, courageous. If afflicted, sickness through privation or neglect; troubles through subordinates. If Mars is the afflicting planet, dangerous illness and operations. If Rahu afflicts, the person suffers from hysteria. Saturn well-aspected denotes gains through contract work, mining masonry, etc.

Rahu.—Long-lived and wealthy, troubled by enemies, ghosts and diseases in private parts. He will also suffer from sickness of a puzzling nature. There is also liability to mental derangement if the Moon and Saturn join Rahu. The person will have many cousins and his private life will be scandalous.

Ketu.—The best position for Ketu to occupy in a horoscope. The person will have fame and authority. He will be foeless. Nevertheless his moral character will be loose. The position also confers intuitive and occult powers.

A word of caution is necessary. Over-enthusiastic students of astrology should not apply the above combinations verbatim and arrive at premature conclusions. The results supposed to be given by the Sun and other

planets occupying the sixth house get modified by a
number of other factors such as aspects, associations, etc.,
of other planets and the general strength or otherwise of
the sixth bhava. If the Sun in the 6th is afflicted in a
fixed sign, heart trouble, asthma, etc., may result. If in a
movable sign, weak chest and poor digestion may result.
A good aspect of Jupiter may neutralise all the results
attributed to the situation of the Sun in the 6th house and
render him capable of conferring quite the opposite results
during his own Bhukti. Success and promotion are sure
to happen when the Sun is aspected by Jupiter. If the
Moon is fortified, that is well disposed, success in the
avocations ruled by the Moon can be anticipated. Moon
afflicted by Rahu denotes skin troubles; by Saturn, chronic
complaints; by Sun, poor digestion; by Rahu or Ketu,
mental derangement, hysteria or peculiar psychic conditions. Mars afflicted by Rahu or Ketu, denotes tendency
for suicide or death by poisoning. Mars well disposed is
an asset in the horoscope. Saturn afflicting Mars favours
litigation with brothers and cousins. Mercury fortified
sharpens the intellect ; joined by Jupiter, spiritual gains
may be anticipated. Afflicted by Rahu, Ketu or Saturn,
despondency, excitability and abnormal mental behaviour
may be anticipated. Jupiter afflicted causes hardships and
intemperance in food habits. Venus, well placed, favours
success in nursing, films or drama. Afflicted, the person
suffers from urinary and sexual troubles. Dangerous
illness, incurable diseases, undiagnosable psychic conditions are the results of Saturn's affliction. Between Rahu
and Ketu, the latter's position is to be preferred in the
6th. Rahu's affliction is the most unfortunate combination
denoting huge debts, unexpected enmities and incurable
diseases. Affliction of Rahu by Saturn and Moon together
should be dreaded, unless there is relief by benefic asso-

ciations or aspects, as it will make the native a psychological misfit. The native will be very sensitive to environment, gets easily excited and irritated. In all these cases, a careful evaluation of the influences involved is absolutely necessary.

Summing up, the 6th has mainly to do with the three important arishtas or misfortunes, *viz.*, diseases, debts and enemies. The combinations dealing with diseases are innumerable and they will form the subject-matter of a separate book entitled *Medical Astrology*, which I have planned to write. In this book, I shall deal with some important diseases, with suitable illustrations.

Karma finds manifestation on physical, mental and spiritual planes. The resultant of evil Karma on the physical plane is disease and medicine is the first *shanti* or remedial measure for the alleviation of human suffering.

The fundamental purpose of medical astrology is to give the planetary influences which cause the various diseases, afflictions and accidents. In ancient times all doctors were expected to know astrology and its relation to disease, what diseases would be produced under different planetary conditions, the duration of such diseases and whether or not they would prove fatal. Modern doctors would do well to lay aside their prejudices and make use of astrology for the diagnosis and treatment of diseases. When properly applied astrology would quickly determine the seat of disease in the patient. Diseases may be classed under two heads—inherent and active. Inherent tendencies to diseases are shown by the afflictions in the birth horoscope. These tendencies may remain latent for long periods and then appear when the directions of evil planets are in progress. On the other hand, the 'active diseases' may make their appearance with every evil transit, if the Lagna is weak and afflicted.

Every student of astrology must recognise the importance of mental influence upon bodily ailment. The Moon rules over the mind, the Lagna represents the body and the Sun governs the soul so that when the Moon and the Sun are strong and free from affliction, one can enjoy sound health even if the Lagna is subject to unfavourable aspects and conjunctions. All these days, modern medicine had been persistently preaching that all diseases were curable by drugs. Ayurveda, on the other hand, had recognised that physical disease was interdependent upon the mind and insisted that mental harmony was the *sine qua non* of health and well-being. That is why great stress was laid by ancients on the strength of the Moon in the horoscope. Sir Walter Langdon Brown, Regius Professor of Physics in the University of Cambridge, is reported to have observed that "drugs are not the whole of medicine. The dualism of mind and body has broken down under the assaults of psychologically-minded physicians. The doctors of the future will have to come doubly armed with material aid for physical troubles and psychotherapy for distresses of the spirit". In other words, modern medicine is only returning to the point of view held by the sages five thousand years ago that health depends on harmony and disease upon discord between the body and mind.

The first thing for an astrologer is to study the Moon and thereby the mental qualities of a patient. Note the sign in which the Moon is placed, the house, and the arishtas and yogas to which he is subject. The secondary determinant of mental qualities is of course Mercury, as he is the ruler of the nerves and the nervous system. The basic qualities of these two planets in the signs should be very carefully studied. Harmonious relationship between these two planets is a great asset. If the Moon is in conjunction with Saturn and there is no beneficial aspect to

relieve, the mind is stubborn, slow and subject to melancholia. When however there is *Adhi Yoga* or *Gajakesari
Yoga*, a well-balanced mind with good reasoning qualities
will develop and a retentive memory is shown. Mars in
intimate contact (association or aspect) with the Moon
shows that the person is of a high, strong, emotional,
erratic type with little control over the mind. Chandra-
Chandala Yoga, resulting by Rahu–Moon association,
suggests that the mind is inclined towards unhealthy and
unnatural conditions, obsession, religious mania, medium-
ship, drugs, vices and so on. How these tendencies
express themselves depends upon the houses and the signs.
When, for instance, the Moon is in Scorpio and is afflicted
by Saturn or Rahu, the native is often tempted to use
black-magic and may himself become the victim of those
who unscrupulously make use of these dreadful practices.
Again, when the Moon is severely afflicted by Rahu or
Saturn, the person will have a sort of 'hysteria' as it may
give the mind suicidal tendencies owing to extreme sensi-
tiveness or short temper. The psychological set-up is therefore of the utmost importance before the predisposition
to physical diseases is considered.

It must be made very clear that a 'mental' diagnosis
should never be made on the basis of one or two combinations. The entire horoscope should be considered
carefully.

Before taking up the 'diagnosis' proper, a few observations seem to be necessary. The strongest planet in the
horoscope determines the predominance of the physical,
mental and spiritual peculiarities of the person. Thus if
the Sun is the strongest planet, the native enjoys well-
balanced health, looks only at the bright side of things.
The weak point is the eyesight. He is likely to suffer from
accidents due to fire. However, if the Sun is predominantly

weak one may become blind, the heart will be in a poor condition. He will be frequently troubled with palpitations and aneurism. He may be a victim of sunstroke. When Mars is very strong in the horoscope, the sanguine temperament is represented. The blood is rich. Apoplexy, skin disease, inflammation of the inner orgnas are the likely complaints. He runs a great risk of wounds in quarrels. When Mars is highly afflicted, the native may commit acts which may lead him to the scaffold. The *Mercury-man* is endowed with a bilious temperament. His weak points are the nervous system, liver and digestive organs. He is sometimes childishly superstitious and has a tendency to go in for quick remedies. When Jupiter is the strongest planet, the temperament is both phlegmatic and sanguine. One may suffer from excessive indulgeace in eating and drinking. The Venus person is strong, healthy and happy, sensual, fond of the good things of life. The disposition is cheerful. He may suffer from disappointments in love, derangements of the generative organs. At worst, he will suffer from the consequences of his excesses and has to pay for them dearly. Syphilis, blood-poisoning, etc., are not outside possibilities. When Saturn is the strongest planet, one may often suffer from vericose veins. He worries a great deal and suffers from chronic melancholia that may sometimes grow into insanity. Unclean in habits, uncouth in appearance with rough hair all over the body, lean and tall, inactive, one is apt to make himself an undesirable visitor. The spinal column requires special care.

Time of Fructificatihn of the Results of the Sixth House

In timing events pertaining to the 6th house, factors to be considered are :—

(a) The lord, (b) the planet or planets aspecting the house, (c) planet or planets posited in the 6th house, (d) planets aspecting the lord of the 6th house (e) planet or planets in association with the lord of the 6th, (f) the lord of the 6th from the Moon and the karaka of the 6th.

The factors mentioned above are capable of influencing the 6th house, as lords of main periods (Dasas), as lords of sub-periods (Bhuktis) or as lords of still minor periods.

The sub-periods of planets capable of influencing the 6th house, in the major periods of planets also capable of influencing the 6th, produce results pertaining to the 6th house *par excellence*. The sub-periods of planets associated with the 6th house in the major periods of planets not associated with the 6th house can produce results pertaining to the 6th house only to a limited extent. Similarly the sub-periods of lords who have nothing to do with the 6th in the major periods of lords, associated with the 6th, can produce results pertaining to the 6th only to a limited or small extent.

Nature of Results

In general, the following results are likely to happen in the periods and sub-periods of planets capable of influencing the 6th house, subject to other peculiarities of the horoscope concerned.

When the 6th lord is in the 6th, fortified, generally beneficial results will happen during the Dasa. The results likely to happen during the sub-period of a planet, joining the above combination, would be unfavourable, and the results pertain to the nature of the house owned by the conjoined planet. Thus if the 2nd lord joins, there will be financial losses and debts during his sub-period. If the 10th lord joins, there will be reverses in profession. In the

17

sub-periods of planets, not joining the 6th lord in the 6th fairly auspicious results pertaining to the several bhavas owned by the sub-lords will transpire. Financial prosperity can be anticipated during the Dasa of the 6th lord in the 6th, if he is joined by the lords of the 8th and 12th. Happy results will be produced throughout the Dasa.

When the 6th lord joins the 7th and is fortified, mixed results will happen during his Dasa; there will be trouble from enemies for some time and the person will also become free from these troubles. When on tour he will meet with disappointments and obstacles. When the 6th lord joins the 7th lord in the 7th, the subject or his wife will suffer from ill-health. Or in his own sub-period, misunderstandings with wife may arise. If a malefic also joins this combination and in addition to this Lagnadhipati is weak, the person will fall seriously ill, there will be misunderstandings, troubles from enemies. indebtedness and in the case of women, female complaints. If the Navamsa held by the 6th lord is in the 6th, 8th or 12th, misunderstandings with wife; if the 6th lord is in the 5th, 7th, 9th or 10th Navamsa, wife's character will be suspect. If in addition to the above affliction, the 6th house is a common sign and the lord is in a common Navamsa, he will divorce the wife and remarry. If Venus joins the above combination then due to misunderstandings with wife, he will have sex connections with other women. When the 6th lord is as above stated and joined by the 2nd lord, the person is likely to die in the 6th lord's major period and the 2nd lord's sub-period.

When the 6th lord is in the 8th, well disposed, favourable results happen during the sub-periods of benefic planets. When lord of Lagna is in the 6th and lord of 6th is in the 8th, then during the sub-period of Lagnadhipati within the major period of the 6th lord, the person suffers from incurable diseases, poverty, loss of money and distress of mind. However, if the Lagnadhipati occupies the 6th, 8th or 12th Navamsa, in a benefic sign, there will be redemption from ailments and suffering. No relief can be expected from the unfortunate results suggested above if the lord of Lagna joins the lord of 6th or 8th or if they are in conjunction in Navamsa. The significations of the bhava, whose lord joins the 6th lord in the 8th, will be destroyed during the sub-period of the former in the major period of the latter. Suppose lord of the 10th joins the 6th lord in the 8th. Then in the sub-period of the 10th lord in the Dasa of the 6th lord, there will be reverses in profession or loss of occupation, etc.

When the 6th lord is in the 9th, joined by malefics, and Pitrukaraka (Sun) is strongly disposed, the father faces misfortunes, danger from enemies, mental anguish and heavy losses. The father may lose property, face pecuniary troubles and litigation and get involved in debts. Father will die in the major period of the 6th lord and the sub-period of the Sun if he joins the 6th lord in the 9th. When the 6th lord is in the 9th, and the Sun joined by the 9th lord is in the 8th or, being weak, the lord (in the 9th) is associated with or aspected by the 8th lord, father's death will be due to swelling and inflammation of abdomen. When the 7th lord also joins the above combination, father will not die but he will become inimically disposed towards his son.

When the 6th lord is in the 10th in association with the 10th lord, then his day-to-day professional activities will be dislocated. He will take to occupations considered low and degrading by current social values. He will incur the displeasure of the Government or his superiors and may become a victim of calumny. If, however, the 10th lord is in the 6th, 8th or 10th in Navamsa, aspected or joined by benefics, the above evil results will be lessened. Afflicted, the maximum of evil will happen.

When the 6th lord occupies the 11th with the 11th lord, his gains in business, agriculture or in his occupation in general, will be below normal. These results will happen specially during the sub-period of the 6th lord. When the 6th lord is fortified, there will be gains from the maternal uncle, but he will incur the displeasure of his own elder brothers. If the 11th lord is stronger than the 6th lord, he will conquer his enemies and overcome all opposition.

When the 6th lord occupies the 12th with the 12th lord, he will suffer from troubles, losses and destruction in his enemies' hands. He will become immoral. The affliction will come from the source denoted by the bhava lord joining the above combination. When the 6th lord is fortified, no untoward things will happen.

When the 6th lord is in Lagna in conjunction with the lord of Lagna, the native will suffer from diseases or deformity to an organ, troubles from his superiors and machinations of enemies. When Rahu joins the above combination, he will lose by theft, and will have to face poverty and penury. If the 6th lord occupies the 6th, 8th or 12th from Lagnadhipati (in Navamsa) there will be a tempering of the evil results suggested above. He will have sharp attacks or misfortune, ill-health and financial losses continuously one after the other during the Dasa of the 6th lord if the 8th lord also joins the 6th lord in Lagna or the 6th and 8th lords are on either side of the Navamsa Lagna or Lagnadhipati in Navamsa. Under the above set-up, life becomes hell and the native will meet with untimely death.

When the 6th lord is in the 2nd with the 2nd lord, family life will be disrupted. Relatives and friends will turn into bitter enemies. He will not have timely meals.

There will be loss of money through enemies. He will suffer from dental and eye troubles or cancer. When any benefics join the above combination, troubles and auspicious events will alternately happen when Lagnadhipati joins the combination and no benefic influences are involved, then death can be predicted in the Dasa' of the 6th lord and Bhukti of Lagnadhipati. Consistent with the nature of the sum-total of influences involved in the above combination, either death or most adverse events will take place.

When the 6th lord joins the 3rd lord in the 3rd, the person will have misunderstandings with his brothers. He will have ear or throat complaints or deafness or injuries to the neck, lose self-confidence and incur the enmity of friends. When benefics join, there will be a lessening of these evil effects. When Mars is weak, brothers will suffer from illness or death.

When the 6th lord is in the 4th, and Rahu and the Moon are together, mother's honour will be at stake during the Dasa of the 6th lord. If the Dasa comes late in life, the person's health will be in great jeopardy. When Mars is weak, the native's immovable properties will be auctioned or lost to his enemies. If Mercury is weak, he will fail in examinations or there will be breaks in education. If Venus is weak, he will meet with accidents by falling from vehicles. When the 4th lord is strong, mother may become a widow. When lords of Lagna and the 4th are in the 6th and 8th from each other, the person will separate from his mother. Other benefic or malefic influences will lessen or increase the intensity of the evil results suggested above.

When the 6th lord is in the 5th in conjunction with the 5th lord he will incur the enmity of his boss or son or father consistent with the karaka nature of these lords.

His children will frequently suffer ill-health. He will meet with all sorts of obstructions. His thinking will be perverted. Spiritual practices, if taken to, during this Dasa, will prove abortive. If the 6th lord posited in the 5th occupies the 4th, 5th, 7th, 9th or 11th degree and lord of Lagna is weak and afflicted, then the person will incur the displeasure of the rulers and suffer imprisonment in the Dasa of the 6th lord and the Bhukti of Lagnadhipati or *vice versa*.

In interpreting Dasa results pertaining to any bhava, emphasis is laid by the sages on yukti or *interpretative skill*. It is an admitted fact that in order to examine a horoscope a good deal of judgment is required. The strength of the planets, their various aspects and the innumerable influences have to be properly weighed, appropriate evidence sifted and then the inference drawn. For instance, the rules given above for predicting the results likely to happen during the Dasa of the lord of a particular bhava can merely serve as a code of reference. With these at his command, the clever reader will have to use his discretion and lay down a ruling as he can best draw a conclusion from them. The greatest mistake that one can commit is to apply verbatim the principles to actual charts.

It has been given above that when the lord of the 6th joins the 5th lord in the 5th, the person will incur the enmity of his son or father. Supposing, Lagna is Pisces. Then the 6th lord will be the Sun, who is Pitrukaraka and the 5th lord is the Moon who is Matrukaraka. The association having reference to 5th house, or Cancer, the Moon is well placed. During the Dasa of the Sun, therefore, the person, whose enmity will be incurred, will of course be the father of the native.

Suppose in the above case, the Sun is in the 4th, 7th or 5th, 9th or 10th degree. Then the person will suffer imprisonment in Moon Bhukti in Sun Dasa, for offences indicated by the karaka planets, aspecting or associated with this combination.

As we have said above, the sixth house has mainly to do with diseases, debts and enemies. We shall deal with a few salient principles of medical astrology and give a number of charts illustrative of certain important diseases, debts and enemies severally. Methods of diagnosis of diseases, time of their occurrence and disappearance will be exhaustively dealt with in our work, MEDICAL ASTROLOGY, under preparation now.

Three seats of disease are recognised, viz., if the Lagna is movable and belongs to Urdhwamukha Rasi, then the disease can be seen above the neck ; if fixed and Thiryugmukha, the disease is below the neck and above the waist, and if it is common and Adhomukha the disease will be below the waist. The following planets govern the organs mentioned against them :

The Sun - stomach ; the Moon—heart ; Mars—head ; Mercury—chest ; Jupiter- thighs ; Saturn—legs, and the bones tibia and fibula ; and Rahu—the feet. Zodiacal allocation of organs is similar to the method adopted by Varahamihira, viz., Aries or Lagna ruling head and so on.

The Thridoshas are governed by different planets as follows :

The Sun—Mostly pitta (bile) and a little of vatha (wind).

The Moon—Mostly vatha (wind) and a little of kapha (phlegm).

Mars—Pitta (bile).

Mercury—Mostly vatha (wind), a little of pitta (bile) and still less of kapha (phlegm).

Jupiter—More of kapha (phlegm) and a little of vatha (wind).

Venus—More of vatha (wind) and a little of kapha (phlegm).

Saturn—More of vatha (wind) and a little pitta (bile).

Examine carefully the horoscope. If the Sun and Mars occupy evil places, diseases by pitta (extreme heat, etc.), can be seen. The Moon and Venus if evil by position bring in diseases caused by water such as swelling, dropsy, water in the head, etc. Saturn brings about diseases pertaining to vatha or wind. Mercury causes brain-fever, typhoid and the like. Jupiter causes deafness. The diseases will make their appearance during the seasons indicated by the planets which are follows :—

Planet	Season	English Equivalent
Venus	Vasantha	Spring
Sun and Mars	Grishma	Summer
Moon	Varsha	Rainy season
Mercury	Sarat	Autumn
Jupiter	Hemantha	Winter
Saturn	Sisira	Winter

Diseases can be read from (a) planets in the 6th, 8th and 12th; (b) planets in association with lord of Lagna; (c) planets aspecting the lord of Lagna; and (d) planets occupying or aspecting Lagna.

The diseases of the various planets are detailed thus: The Sun governs excessive heat and internal fever. The Moon rules 'vomiting' if he is in Urdhwamukha Rasi; diseases in the kidneys and urethra if he is in Thriyugmukha; diarrhoea and thirst if he occupies an Adhomukha Rasi.

Mars or Kuja causes diseases brought about by extreme heat in the body or by impure blood. Mercury or Budha-shivering fever, typhoid, madness ; Jupiter or Guru

—inability to think or remember; Venus or Sukra—Indigestion, water in the body, extreme heat in the body, fits and swoons; Sani or Saturn—Thirst, aversion to eat or drink, pain in all parts of the body; Rahu—Difficulties in breathing; Gulika—Contraction of the nerves; and Ketu —Same as Rahu.

Diseases can be classified into several kinds such as Sariraka (bodily), Chithothara (mental), those caused by the three doshas individually and those caused by a permutation and combination of the three doshas and so on.

According to the famous work PRASNA MARGA bodily diseases can be ascertained by an examination of (a) the 8th house, (b) the lord of the 8th, (c) the planet who aspects the 8th, and (d) the planet who occupies the 8th. The strongest of these will cause the disease pertaining to the dosha under its domain and in the particular organ governed by the zodiacal sign it afflicts.

PRASNA MARGA further says that if the Sun occupies an Arishtasthana, troubles from pitta, fever with pains, sudden fall, apasmara, heart disease, diseases in the stomach, diseases in the eyes, fear from enemies, skin diseases, Asthi diseases (dislocation of bones, etc.), leprosy, fear from Gurus, troubles from weapons, danger from poison, death of one's wife, danger to the son, danger from quadrupeds, trouble from thieves, fear from kings, anger of the family deity, anger of the serpent gods, evil influence of Bhutas (certain evil spirits) will happen.

If the Moon occupies an evil position, then increase of sleep, want of agility in any work (inertia), increase of phlegm, and consequent troubles such as asthma, inflammation of the lungs, etc., diarrhoea, sores and boils, shivering fever; wounds caused by the horns of animals, troubles from watery animals, dyspepsia, emaciation, sorrow from wife, want of blood in the body, weakness in thinking faculty, poisoning of the blood and consequent diseases, fear from water, troubles from Balagrahas, anger of the Goddess Durga, anger of family gods or deities, anger of serpents, etc.

Evil Mars brings about thirst, blood pressure, pitta, fever, diseases caused by heat, fire, poison and weapons; leprosy, sore-eye, gulma (a disease in the stomach), apasmara—decline of Majja in the bones; skin loses its lustre, itches all over the body, body gets shrivelled, troubles from kings, enemies and thieves; enmity with brothers, sons and relatives, and diseases above the neck.

An unfavourable Mercury causes madness, an inclination to use abusive words often. Diseases in the eye, diseases in the throat and the nose, high fever caused by the fury of all the doshas—fear from serpents, fear from poison, skin diseases, dull pallor, bad dreams, itches; sudden falling down, a tendency to use cruel expressions—fear of imprisonment, physical exertion—evil influences such as Pakshi Peeda, etc.

Jupiter or Guru if afflicted brings about gulma (disease in the stomach), fever, sorrow, fainting, ear diseases due to the fury of kapha dosha; diabetes, diseases caused by the curses of Brahmins and by the removal of treasure usually found in temples, and diseases by the anger of serpents.

A bad Venus brings in pandu (a sort of leucoderma), diseases caused by the fury of phlegm and wind, diseases in the eye, laziness, great exertion for the body and consequent weakness, diseases in the private organs, diseases in the face, diseases in the urinary organs; danger caused by extreme averse for money or girls, free flow of seminal fluid (spermatorrhoea), loss of clothes and dress, death of wife, loss in cultivation, fading away of the lustre in the body, swelling of the body, fear from certain evil spirits, death of near relations.

An afflicted Saturn gives diseases caused by vatha and kapha, diseases in the legs, unforeseen dangers, laziness, weakness, due to over-exertion, madness, pains or aches in the stomach, loss of servants, loss of quadrupeds —death of wife and children—some accident to one of the limbs in the body, blindness, deafness, mental worry, wounds caused by the fall of trees or stones over the body, troubles from evil spirits, pisachas, etc.

If Rahu occupies an unfavourable house, then extreme heat in the body, leprosy, Vishama vyadhi (many diseases coming together), poison given by another, diseases in the feet, trouble from pisachas, fear from serpents, danger from wife and children, quarrel with Kshatriyas and Brahmins, trouble from enemies, and trouble from pretas (ghosts).

Gulika gives all the troubles caused by Rahu and Ketu and besides it brings in anger of all. Death of near relations and consequent pollution and fear from poison (mad dogs also should be included) may also be anticipated.

If Saturn is in the 10th house predict trouble from pisachas and pakshi peeda. If Gulika occupies Lagna or the 8th house and he is aspected by Rahu, then predict poison in the body caused by swelling or evil eye. If evil planets occupy the 6th house, predict diseases in the stomach. Mars in the 8th house causes fever; in Lagna indigestion, and in the 7th house, both.

Mental diseases are caused by anger, fear, sorrow, and desires. These have to be determined by the mutual dispositions of the lords of the 5th and 8th.

Then there is another class of diseases caused by invisible agencies such as spirits, curses of great men and mantric incantations of enemies.

The above diseases have to be ascertained by an examination of the 6th house, or its lord, the planet that aspects the lord of the 6th house, or the planet occupying the 6th. If the 6th and 8th lords are in conjunction or aspect each other, then say that the disease is strong and deep-rooted.

The following astrological combinations indicate different forms of lunacy :

1. Vathonmada (lunacy caused by the excitation of the dosha wind).—This can be detected by the following symptoms, viz., laughing at all moments, clapping hands often, speaking aloud, dancing round and round, crying bitterly, shaking legs and wringing hands. The body becomes copper coloured, soft and emaciated. He becomes more turbulent as soon as the food taken in is digested.

2. Pittonmada (lunacy caused by excitation of the dosha bile). — Symptoms : Hates all, impertinent, flying into a rage at the face of all, showering abuses, always longing to eat food and drink water, very angry. The body becomes yellow and feels hot when it is felt.

3. Kaphonmada (excitation of phlegm) —Symptoms: Seeking solitude and women, aversion to everything, little sleep, saliva trickling down always, finger-nails turning pale and white.

4. Sannipathonmada (excitation of all the three doshas).—The symptoms mentioned above will be found in a mixed form. Recovery of one suffering Sannipatha is almost impossible.

All the above forms of madness can be ascertained by the following 8 kinds of planetary combinations :—
(1) Jupiter in Lagna and Saturn in the 7th ; (2) Jupiter in Lagna and Mars in the 7th ; (3) Saturn in Lagna and Mars in the 7th or 5th or 9th ; (4) the Moon and Mercury in combination occupying Lagna ; (5) weak Moon and Saturn in the 12th ; (6) weak Moon in conjunction with

an evil planet occupying Lagna, 5th, 8th or 9th; (7) Gulika in the 7th in conjunction with an evil planet; and (8) Mercury occupying 3rd, 6th, 8th or 12th in conjunction with evil planets.

Vatha, Pitta and Kapha Unmadas are said to be curable by administring medicines in judicious quantities but Sannipathonmada is said to be incurable except by mantraic treatment, japa, homa, wearing talismans, etc.

If the Moon, Venus and lord of 8th occupy evil places, infer that lunacy is due to irregular use of food. If the above planets are with Rahu, Ketu or Gulika, the madness is due to unhygienic food. If Mars is in the 5th, the cause is due to excess of anger; any other evil planet suggests excess of fear. If evil planets are in the 9th, consider that madness is the outcome of curses of Gurus and elderly people.

Chart No. 109.—Born on 28-1-1919 at 3-58 p.m. (I.S.T.) (Lat. 22° 40' N., Long. 88° 30' E.)

	Ketu Mandi	Lagna Jupit.		Moon	Lagna Sun Saturn	Ketu Mandi
Mars Venus		Jupit.				
	RASI			AMSA		
Sun		Sat.				
Moon Merc.	Rahu			Rahu Mars Merc.	Venus	

Balance of Ketu Dasa at birth : Years 5-5-0.

Remarks.—Suffered from a severe type of typhoid fever in Venus Dasa, Venus Bhukti, Saturn Antara. Note Venus is in association with the lord of the 6th Mars and aspected by Saturn lord of the 8th. Saturn was transiting Scorpio. From the Moon, Venus happens to be the 6th lord and occupies the 6th in the Navamsa. In Venus Dasa, Saturn was transiting Aquarius he suffered from pneumonia, and loss of weight and T.B. was suspected. Subsequently in the Dasa of the Sun (note the Sun being lord of the 3rd is in the 8th, in the 12th from Mars, karaka of the 6th bhava) the native again suffered from malignant malaria, pneumonia and awful blood vomiting.

Chart No. 110.—*Born on 2/3-9-1921 at ⁻3 a.m. (I.S.T.) (Lat. 8° 45' N., Long. 73° 45' E.)*

				Mars Ketu		
Ketu						
			Lagna Mars Venus	Jupit. Sat.		Lagna
	RASI				AMSA	
			Sun Moon Merc. Mandi			
			Jupit. Rahu Sat.	Moon Mandi Merc.	Venus	Sun Rahu

Balance of Sun Dasa at birth : Years 4–11–9.

The above is the horoscope of an intelligent hard-working lady, an M.A., B.T., who remained unmarried and died in her 27th year. T.B. was suspected in 1947 in Rahu Dasa, Jupiter Bhukti, Sun Antara. Rahu, the major lord, is in association with Jupiter lord of the 6th from

Lagna and Saturn lord of the 6th from Chandra Lagna.
Jupiter as sub-lord is fully capable of causing the disease
which he has done. The Sun is Chandra Lagnadhipathi
and occupies the 12th from the major and minor lords.
Saturn was transiting Cancer. As soon as the sub-period
of Saturn commenced, she died. Mark the fact Saturn is
lord of the 7th from Moon and is Ayushkaraka. At the
time of her death, Saturn was transiting Leo and Rahu
Aries, the 8th from Janma Rasi.

Chart No. 111.—*Born on 26-7-1914 at 5-24 p.m.
(I.S.T.) (Lat. 29° N., Long. 77° 40' E.)*

			Merc. Sat.	Sun			Merc.
Rahu		RASI	Sun	Rahu		AMSA	
Jupit.			Ketu Moon Mars Venus				Lagna Ketu Mandi
Lagna Mandi				Mars	Moon Saturn	Venus	Jupit.

Balance of Venus Dasa at birth : Years 2-3-18.

The native had an attack of T.B. in Moon Dasa,
Venus Bhukti, Sun Antara. The major lord Moon,
owning the 8th, is in the 9th in conjunction with Venus
the sub-lord who owns the 6th and Mars (karaka for 6th
bhava) and with Ketu. The Sun is in the 8th from Lagna
having Dwirdwadasa position from major and sub-lords.
This combination is aspected by Saturn lord of the 6th
from Chandra Lagna.

From 1930 to 1934 he went to jail five times in connection with political movements. The first conviction took place in Moon Dasa Mercury Bhukti. Note Mercury is also afflicted. By virtue of the association of the Moon and Venus, as lord of the 6th and 11th, the native had to suffer imprisonment. Mars and Rahu are also involved in this combination. Consequently he continued to be jailed during Mars Dasa, Mars and Rahu sub-periods also.

Chart No. 112.—*Born on 15-6-1912 at 5-23 a.m. (I.S.T.) (Lat. 25° 23' N., Long. 86° 31' E.)*

Rahu	Mercury Venus Moon Saturn	Lagna Sun Mandi	Rahu		
		Mars	Sat. Mandi		
	RASI		AMSA		
					Venus
	Jupiter	Ketu	Lagna Jupit.	Sun	Moon Mars Ketu Merc.

Balance of Mars Dasa at birth : Years 4–3–29.

The lord of the 6th Mars is in the 2nd (vision) and lord of the 2nd Moon (ruler of eyes) is in the 12th with Saturn, lord of the 8th. The native is suffering from myopia.

Mark the disposition of the 6th house in Chart No. 113. The 6th lord Mars, who also happens to be the Rogakaraka, is in the 11th with malefics Saturn, Ketu and the Sun. There is slight relief as Jupiter aspects this combination. In Sun Dasa Moon Bhukti, the native had

Chart No. 113.—*Born on 7-10-1893 at 8-30 a.m. (L.M.T.) (Lat. 16° 57' N., Long. 82° 13' E.)*

Rahu	Jupiter		Rahu	Mars Jupiter	
					Sun Lagna Venus Mandi
	RASI			AMSA	Sat.
		Moon			
Lagna Mandi Venus	Mercury	Sun Mars Sat. Ketu		Mercury	Moon	Ketu

Balance of Venus Dasa at birth : Years 9–2–21.

Chart No. 114.—*Born on 9-9-1911 at 11-18 p.m. (I.S.T.) (Lat. 22° 53' N., Long. 88° 27' E.)*

Moon	Saturn Rahu	Mars	Lagna Mandi	Jupit.	Mars	
				Venus		Rahu
	RASI			AMSA	
		Sun Merc.		Ketu	
	Jupiter Ketu	Venus	Sat.	Sun Mercury	Lagna Mandi	Moon

Balance of Saturn Dasa at birth : Years 12–5–27.

18

a serious attack of smallpox. Mark the association of the Sun with the 6th lord and the other afflictions he has been subject to.

The lord of the 6th Mars, who is also the Rogakaraka, is in the 12th aspecting the 6th (Chart No. 114). From the Moon the 6th and the 6th lord are aspected by Mars. Lord of Lagna Mercury and lord of vitality the Sun are both aspected by Mars. Throughout Saturn Dasa (for the first 12 years) the native suffered from liver and spleen troubles. Mark the fact that Saturn is lord of the 8th and is with Rahu, of course, aspected by Jupiter. Venus, lord of the 8th from the Moon is neecha and subject to Papakarthari Yoga. Mercury the planet of nerves is considerably afflicted. Throughout Mercury Dasa he was the victim of serious spermatorrhoea. In Mercury Dasa Venus Bhukti, he had hydrocele and he was operated upon for this in Mercury Dasa, Jupiter Bhukti. Mercury as Lagnadhipathi is afflicted by association with Sun lord of the 3rd and aspected by Mars lord of the 6th while Jupiter is afflicted by being aspected by Saturn, lord of the 8th and by Rahu. At the time of the operation, Saturn was transiting Janma Rasi.

In Venus Dasa, Rahu Bhukti the native had a serious attack of typhoid. (Chart No. 115) Venus, the major lord, owns the Lagna as well as the 6th and occupies the 2nd with Saturn. Venus and Saturn are almost in conjunction. In the same Dasa, Saturn Bhukti he had an attack of bronchitis. Mark the disposition of the 6th lord and Saturn in Gemini, an airy sign.

In Chart No. 116 the 6th is occupied by Ketu while the Moon is in Virgo subjected to powerful Papakarthari Yoga. The 6th lord Sun is in the 2nd with Mercury lord of the 4th. The 6th from the Moon is occupied by Rahu

Chart No. 115.—*Born on 19-5-1916 at 6-10 a.m. (I.S.T.) (Lat. 22° 1' N., Long. 82° 4' E.)*

	Jupiter	Lagna Sun Mercury	Venus Sat. Mandi	Venus	Jupiter Saturn Mandi Rahu	Mars	Lagna
			Ketu	Sun Moon			
Rahu		RASI			AMSA		Merc.
			Mars				
	Moon						Ketu

Balance of Mercury Dasa at birth : Years 4–6–9.

Chart No. 116.—*Born on 4/5-5-1895 at 4-00 a.m. (L.M.T.) (Lat. 13° 2' N., Long. 77° 35' E.)*

Lagna	Sun Mercury	Mars Venus Jupit.	Mars				Rahu
Rahu					AMSA		
	RASI		Jupit. Moon Sat.				
		Ketu	Ketu	Mercury		Lagna Sun Venus	
	Saturn	Moon					

Balance of Sun Dasa at birth : Years 4–5–19.

and the 6th lord Saturn is in the 2nd from the Moon aspected by Sun and Mercury. Therefore the liability to attack by appendicitis is plain and unmistakable.

As we have already said above, Ketu is in the 6th ruling abdomen. Saturn is in the 8th house. The native underwent an emergency operation for appendicitis about August 1926 which terminated fatally. Rahu's position in the 6th from the Moon is equally indicative of predisposition for appendicitis. The operation took place and death occurred in the Dasa of Rahu and sub-period of Venus. Rahu is to give the results of Saturn and Saturn is in a house of maraka or death from the Moon. Venus is in conjunction with Mars. Added to all this, Mars was transiting Cancer and Saturn Libra. The Elarata influence coupled with poweful mutual aspects between transiting Mars and Saturn all contributed to the acceleration of death.

A few general observations may be made on appendicitis in the light of astrological factors.

According to modern medical explanations, appendicitis is a very prevalent disease, being a condition of inflammation of the vermiform appendix. The appendix seems to be a vestigeal organ that has no function in the anatomy of man in his present state of biological evolution and consequently is an atrophying organ. Appendicitis appears to be, to a decided extent, a disease caused by the affliction of the sixth house and the Moon. *Abdominal diseases, appendicitis, etc., are caused by the movements of the Sun and the Moon in Virgo.

When the 6th house is occupied by a malefic particularly Mars, Ketu or Rahu, disease will be in a latent state. It may gradually develop under the directional

---

* *Hindu Predictive Astrology.*

influences of the planet concerned or the tendencies may be resisted by taking proper precautions from the very beginning in the shape of regulating diet and habits. When the disease becomes acute and dangerous, there will usually be found an affliction in the 5th or 6th house by the transit of Mars and mutual aspects between transiting Mars and transiting Saturn. Obviously, the prevailing Dasa and Bhukti influences provide their quota of evil. The 'tendencies' in the chart take the form of acute disease by the progressed influences. Mars, as we have said above, has a baneful influence on this disease. This is due to his effect upon the adrenal glands. The effect of martian influences on the adrenal glands is to set up a chemical imbalance which may localise in the appendix and set up irritation therein due to the fact that it is shown to be weak and susceptible to irritation and inflammation by the horoscopic indications.

These unfavourable martian influences tend to overwork the adrenal glands and weaken and deplete their harmones, so that the supply of adrenalin and intercortin, the chemical agents which resist infection become insufficient. Pus then begins to form in the appéndix and if this condition increases, the poisons spread through the blood stream and death ensues. This is the dangerous and often fatal stage when septic peritonitis sets in. The septic peritonitis results from the breaking down and decay of the tissues of the appendix—a gangrenous condition.

The affliction of Jupiter in Pisces or Saturn in Virgo or Pisces or Rahu in Scorpio or Mars in Gemini or Virgo, the affliction happening to occur in the 5th or 6th house is likely to bring about appendicitis. It will be seen that the 6th house is not only the general seat of disease but has special governance over the abdomen. Hence a malefic·

of the type of Rahu or Mars is decidedly unfavourable
especially if the sign happens to be Virgo and the Moon is
also there. Summing up our observations, we can say
that the following combinations show a predisposition to
appendicitis :—

(a) Affliction of the 22nd drekkana particularly by
Rahu or Mars.

(b) The sixth house being subjected to powerful
Papakarthari Yoga.

(c) The Moon being posited in Virgo, Scorpio,
Aquarius and subject to malefic influences.

(d) The Sun in Leo or Aquarius receiving the aspect
of Saturn, Mars or Rahu or being associated with any of
these three planets.

In the light of the above principles, one can safely find
out, if any tendencies for appendicitis are to be found in
a horoscope.

Chart No. 117.—*Data of birth withheld for obvious
reasons.*

Ketu			Lagna Sat.	Lagna			
	RASI		Mars	Sat. Rahu	AMSA		
			Sun Merc. Jupit.				Mars Ketu Merc.
		Venus	Moon Rahu	Sun	Jupiter	Venus	Moon

In the typical horoscope we are illustrating herewith,
certain fundamental factors are evident.

The Lagna is Gemini, while in the Navamsa a watery sign rises. The lord of Lagna is in the 3rd with the Sun and Jupiter but afflicted on account of Papakarthari Yoga. Mars, lord of the 6th (disease), is in the 2nd—a watery sign. If we accept the zodiacal rulerships, then we find that the Moon and Rahu in a sensitive place like Virgo, coupled with the presence of Mars in Cancer, suggest the stomach and kidneys as the seat of disease. Saturn being an 'anaemic' planet has the tendency to dry up the body fluids as he is in Lagna. Mark the fact that Venus ruling over sensual appetites, whilst Vargottama, is powerfully aspected by Mars (lord of the 6th) while the 7th from Lagna and Chandra Lagna have unfavourable aspects. Any reasonable astrologer would conclude that these sets of influences indicate that a lack of moral balance was largely responsible for the leprosy of the native. Mercury, who is said to have governance over the thyroid, is aspected by Saturn, and is in association with the Sun (and Jupiter) and hemmed in between Mars and Rahu. Again, Venus the planet of sensual pleasures is in Libra (ruling kidneys) and aspected by Mars. The Moon, one of the planets of vitality, is in a sensitive place and is afflicted by conjunction with Rahu. We may conclude that this man through his excessive desires, indulged in sexual pleasures to such an extent that the functions of the pituitary body became impaired. Saturn is styled lord of sorrow according to the dictum 'duhkham dinesatmajaha', while Rahu is always associated with vice, filth, dirt, etc. With Saturn in Lagna and Rahu with Moon, the Sun being aspected by Saturn, and with Mars, Ketu, Saturn and Rahu in mutual aspect in Navamsa, we can deduce that the native was very untidy, filthy, and unclean in habits and even unmindful of dirty surroundings. The 6th lord Mars is in Leo Navamsa—as usual afflicted. Probably having neglected elimination of toxic poisons through the colon, skin and kidneys, the body was filled with poisons which ultimately caused eruptions. Mercury is lord of skin and he is evilly disposed. Therefore the skin became dry (Mercury in Leo, a dry sign), the mentality dulled (Moon-Rahu conjunction) and the energies of mind and body slowed down.

The above is a case of leprosy in its most dreadful form. Truly have the wise men said that the Lagna must be strong and well aspected, as otherwise, the man would become gluttonous, immoral and careless in personal habits inviting such diseases to take a deeproot in his system.

Readers must be very careful in applying these principles to their own horoscopes lest they should come to premature conclusions based on insufficient knowledge or want of experience. Any antidotes present must be carefully scrutinised before pronouncing judgment.

In the astrological nomenclature, Mars is supposed to originate leprosy. Rahu is of course assumed not only to cause one to suffer from leprosy but to cause death by this dirty disease. Even though the Sun and other planets are not connected with leprosy, it is said to be caused during the sub-period of Mercury in the course of the Sun's Dasa. Obviously one should not rush to the conclusion that it is a definite principle and that every person would suffer from leprosy during Mercury in Sun. The combination suggests that Mercury is also connected with leprosy. Mercury rules the thyroid gland and leprosy is caused by disorders of the thyroid gland. Again leprosy is said to make its appearance during the sub-period of the Moon in the Dasa of Mercury. The disease will definitely make its appearance if Gulika is associated with Saturn. We enumerate below a number of combinations which are said to cause, rather indicate, this dreadful disease.

(1) Mercury in Aries, the Moon in the 10th and Mars and Saturn in conjunction. (2) Saturn, Mars, the Moon and Venus in watery signs, afflicted by conjunction or aspect. (3) The Moon in the 4th from Karakamsa, aspected by Mars. (4) Conjunction of the Sun, Saturn and Mars. (5) The Moon in Mithuna (Gemini), Kataka (Cancer) or Meena (Pisces) Navamsa afflicted by Saturn or Mars. (6) Mercury, the Moon and the lord of Lagna in conjunction with Rahu or Ketu. (7) Mars, Saturn or the Sun and the 6th lord in the ascendant. (8) Mars in Lagna, and Saturn in the 8th, 1st or 4th. (9) Lord of the Lagna in the 8th afflicted by a malefic.

One should be very careful in the application of the above principles to actual horoscopes. For, the operating influence of a combination is subject to the general disposition of the horoscope and the inherent strength or weakness of the factors involved. It is evident from the above information that almost all the planets—Jupiter excluded—come into the picture. Of course, special stress is laid on Mars, Saturn, Rahu, Mercury, the Sun and the Moon. Ketu is less harmful than Rahu. In other words, the Lagna, the Sun, the Moon or Mercury afflicted in any way by the lord of the 6th *plus* a malefic—Rahu, Mars, Saturn or Ketu, should make one suspicious unless other antidotes are present. The above combinations have been taken from authoritative sources. It may not be out of place to mention that our own study and observations extending over a pretty long time bring to the fore the following general causes : (*a*) the Moon in Lagna which should be Aries, afflicted by Saturn, (*b*) Saturn or Mars in the 1st or 7th house in Gemini, Cancer or Pisces, (*c*) Saturn conjunction Mars in Lagna, when the Navamsa of Scorpio, Sagittarius or Capricorn is rising, (*d*) Mercury afflicted in Lagna by the 6th lord, and Rahu or Mars, and (e) the Moon in Virgo, Capricorn and Aquarius afflicted by Mars or Rahu.

There are indeed any number of instances to illustrate the above principles. Our own observations need necessarily have to be taken with due reserve, as in spite of the fact that the deductions are based on the study of a large number of horoscopes, they have to be subjected to far greater studies and tests.

Chart No. 118 is the horoscope of a lady and her trouble is paralysis of the limbs and arms. The 6th is Aries and it is aspected by Mars, the lord of that house. The 6th from the Moon has the Sun (lord of the 6th) with Venus (lord of 3 and 8) and Mercury (ruler of nerves), aspected by Saturn. These afflictions denote the disposition

Chart No. 118.—*Born on 23-8-1899 at 12-10 p.m. (L.M.T.) (Lat. 13° N., Long. 77° 35' E.)*

Moon		Ketu	Mercury Venus	Rahu	Sun Mars
RASI		Jupit. Sat.	AMSA		
		Venus Merc. Sun			
Rahu	Saturn Lagna	Jupiter	Mars	Ketu	Lagna Moon

of the house of disease. Coming to details, the 9th house rules the limbs. Here the 9th from the Moon is Scorpio and the 9th lord Mars aspects the Moon. The 9th is occupied by Saturn, a first-rate malefic. Saturn is the planet of obstruction. Thus the whole region of the lower limbs is afflicted. Saturn aspects the 3rd from Lagna as well as the third from Chandra Lagna, while Mars aspects the 2nd from Lagna as well as from Chandra Lagna. The 3rd rules the arms. The native has plenty of trouble with the arms and limbs. The Sun, ruler of vitality though in his own sign, is associated with the lords of the 8th, 11th, 7th and 12th besides being aspected powerfully by Saturn, lord of the 3rd. Her real troubles started in Saturn Dasa, Rahu Bhukti. There was gradual loss of the limbs, which left her prostrate. Lord of the 6th (and Lagna) Mars in Virgo aspected by the Moon in Pisces gives a tendency to dropsical conditions.

According to Ayurvedic texts facial paralysis is said to be caused by chewing hard substances or loud laughter, or yawning or lying in uneven attitudes. The exciting cause, *viz.*, vatha, pitta or sleshma may be guessed by the

Chart No. 119.—*Born on 12-4-1912 at 12-5 p.m. (I.S.T.) (Lat. 13° N., Long. 77° 35' E.)*

Venus	Sun Rahu Mercury Saturn		Lagna Mars		Sun Rahu	Mercury	Lagna
Moon			Jupit.				
	RASI				AMSA		
			Mars				
	Jupiter	Ketu	Sat.			Moon Ketu	Venus

affliction to which a particular planet having to do with the Lagna or the 6th house is subjected.

Mark the presence of Mars, lord of the 6th in Lagna, almost in exact conjunction with the ascendant point, aspected further by debilitated Saturn. Mars rules mostly pitta while Saturn has reference to more of vatha. Mars in Lagna always suggests some sort of gluttony resulting in indigestion and constipation. When Gochara Saturn passed through Lagna point, facial paralysis set in. As the exciting cause is that of *Mars (pitta), there were, before the stroke of paralysis, frequent attacks of fever, thirst and swoons. Here the diseases may be said to be practically incurable; but still by recourse to medical remedies (dealt with below) and astrological propitiations, some slight relief can be obtained. According to the famous Ptolemy, whose knowledge of astrology is mostly borrowed from India, if malefic planets are in angles and the luminaries are in conjunction or opposition and the Moon is with Rahu or Ketu, the body will be afflicted with lameness or paralysis. A subject in whose chart Jupiter is in Lagna (Aquarius) Saturn in the 7th and Mars in the 6th was paralysed in his 4th year. Based on a study of several horoscopes like the above, we have observed that the following combinations generally show a tendency to suffer from paralytic strokes :

(1) The Sun in Lagna afflicted by Saturn and Mars, particularly in a sign ruling Pitta-humour.

---

* The Thridoshas, *viz.*, Pitta (bile), Vatha (wind) and Sleshma (phlegm) are represented by the twelve signs in an order. That is to say, Aries rules Pitta or bile, Taurus represents Vatha or wind and Gemini signifies Sleshma or phlegm and so on. The Thridoshas are governed by the different planets as follows :—

The Sun.—Mostly Pitta (bile) and a little of Vatha (wind).

The Moon.— Mostly Vatha (wind), and a little of Kapha (phlegm).

Mars.—Pitta (bile).

(2) Saturn–Jupiter combination in the 6th house which should be an airy sign.

(3) The Moon–Mercury conjunction afflicted by Rahu and Saturn.

Diphtheria may be caused if the Lagna is subjected to a severe Papakarthari Yoga, the planets causing the yoga being subjected to powerful afflictions

Then we have the Poliomyelitis or infantile paralysis, a pernicious affliction especially active in India during the last two years. President Roosevelt's horoscope is a good illustration. Mark the afflictions the Sun has received. Rahu in Cancer afflicted by Saturn generally gives rise to infantile paralysis.

Chart No. 120.—*Born on 10/9–7–1902 at 3–45 a.m. (L.M.T.) (Lat. 18° 40' N., Long. 87° 0' E.)*

Ketu	Venus	Mandi Lagna Sun Mars Merc.			Sun	Ketu
	RASI		Sat.	**AMSA**		Venus
Jupit. Sat.		Moon				Jupit.
	Rahu		Rabu Merc.	Moon Mandi	Lagna Mars	

Balance of Venus Dasa at birth : Years 2–9–27.

Mercury.—Mostly Vatha (wind), a little of Pitta (bile) and still less of Kapha (phlegm).

Jupiter.—More of Kapha (phlegm) and a little of Vatha (wind).

Venus.—More of Vatha (wind) and a little of Kapha (phlegm)

Saturn —More of Vatha (wind) and a little of Pitta (bile).

Enormous losses and enormous troubles for the native of the above horoscope coincided with the commencement of Rahu Dasa. Venus whose results Rahu should give is in the 12th while Rahu himself is in the 5th aspected by Saturn, lord of the 8th. In the Navamsa Rahu is aspected by Jupiter, lord of the 6th. Mark the affliction of the 6th lord Mars. He is in Lagna with Mercury, lord of Lagna and the Sun, lord of the 3rd. The man is involved in huge debts.

In Chart No. 121 lord of Lagna and the 6th, viz., Venus is in the 12th with Mars. From Chandra Lagna, the lords of Chandra Lagna and the 6th are in conjunction

Chart No. 121.—*Born on 16-3-1908 at 10-56 a.m. (I.S.T.) (Lat. 15° 24' N., Long. 75° 39' E.)*

Sun Sat.	Mars Venus	Lagna	Rahu	Rahu			
Merc.			Mandi Jupit.				Moon
	RASI		Moon		AMSA		Lagna Sun Venus
Ketu				Merc. Mandi	Mars	Jupiter	Ketu Sat.

Balance of Ketu Dasa at birth : Year 0–0–13.

in the 8th. In the Dasas of the Sun and the Moon the native was convicted several times for political offences. He is a leading and respected Congress man and landlord with spiritual leanings.

Chart No. 122.—*Born on 23-7-1856 at 6-24 a.m. (L.M.T.) (Lat. 18° 32' N., Long. 75° 53' E.)*

Moon Jupit. Rahu		Sat. Merc.	Rahu Sat.	Mercury		
	RASI	Sun Venus Lagna		AMSA		
			Lagna			
	Mars Mandi	Ketu	Moon Jupit.	Mars Mandi	Venus	Sun Ketu

Balance of Mercury Dasa at birth : Years 13-8-14.

The combinations for Bandhana Yoga are clear. Lord of Lagna *viz.*, the Moon is in association with Jupiter lord of the 6th joined by Rahu and aspected by Saturn. The native, a highly respected Indian political leader, underwent long terms of imprisonment for sedition, especially in Sun and Moon Dasas.

Chart No. 123 is the unique case of an ex-cashier of a bank eternally involved in debts. The 6th house is subject to Papakarthari Yoga and the 6th lord Mars is in the 5th with Lagnadhipati, Mercury, Rahu and Venus. In the Navamsa, the afflictions are greater. From Lagna, the 6th is occupied by Saturn while the 6th lord is subjected to Papakarthari Yoga. From Chandra Lagna, the 6th is occupied by Mars and Rahu, the two worst malefics, while the 6th lord Venus is aspected by Saturn and Jupiter. Though he was getting a decent salary, he

Chart No. 123.—*Born on 26/25-9-1901 at 12-20 a.m. (L.M.T.) (Lat. 10° 25' N., Long. 78° 50' E.)*

	Ketu		Lagna	Venus	Lagna Sun	Mars Rahu
Moon		RASI			AMSA	Jupit.
			Mandi			
Jupit. Sat.		Rahu Mars Mercury Venus	Sun	Moon	Ketu	Mercury	Sat. Mandi

Balance of Rahu Dasa at birth :   Years 16-1-18.

contracted innumerable debts, could not pay back his creditors with the result he had to leave his job and roam about to avoid being persecuted by his creditors.

10. Practical Examples

In the various example horoscopes given below, just the essential priciples of bhava-analysis have been applied ignoring the various good and bad yogas and other factors bearing on the horoscopes concerned as I do not want the readers to get confused. The co-ordinates employed in astrology are complex and if unskilfully handled may lead to errors. We have before us the horoscope diagram—Rasi and Navamsa charts, with Bhavasphutas (house-cusps) supplemented with a list of aspects and strengths of planets. The malefic aspects cause affliction and the bene-volent ones gives rise to contrary results. The benefic and malefic nature of planets are to be taken under all con-ceivable relations, both natural and temporal. The lord of the house or bhava is in every way responsible for the control of the bhava. The relations with the lord (Bhava-dhipati) of other planets who have any concern by aspect, association or otherwise have got their own influences to exert. There are a hundred and odd factors to consider and it lies with the astrologer to try the merits thereon. With persistence the difficulties can be overcome and a fairly accurate conclusion arrived at. By way of illustra-tion, we shall analyse in a general manner the 4th, 5th and 6th bhavas respectively in the following horoscopes. The birth details have been withheld for obvious reasons.

Mother.—In Chart No. 124 the fourth house falls in Capricorn with Mercury posited therin. Mercury is the

19

Chart No. 124

Rahu		Moon	Jupit.	Jupit.		Lagna
Sun			Mars	Sun Rahu		
	RASI				AMSA	
Merc.				Moon		Ketu
Sat. Venus		Lagna	Ketu	Venus Sat.		Mars Merc.

Balance of the Sun Dasa at birth :   Years 3–8–27.

Atmakaraka and hence possesses good strength. Saturn lord of the 4th is in the 3rd house aspected by Jupiter, Saturn is in conjunction with benefic Venus. Moon the Matrukaraka is exalted and in the 7th bhava, a kendra. From the Moon the lord of the 4th house is in the 10th aspecting the 4th which is highly beneficial. There are no malefic conjuctions or aspects to the 4th from Moon. From the Lagna in the Navamsa, Ketu is in the 4th. But here again the lord of the 4th aspects the 4th. The 4th from the Moon in the Navamsa falls in Aries the lord of which Mars is in the 9th from the Moon. He too aspects the 4th which being his own sign is good. The lord of the 4th and the Moon have attained Gopuramsa. All this is beneficial and will confer long life on the native's mother. The lord of the 4th house Saturn is in Vargottamamsa. If the Moon be strong or Venus be conjoined with or aspected by a benefic, the mother will live long. Here the Moon is powerful as he is exalted in a kendra and Venus is aspected by Jupiter. So both elements are present though either will do. As for the conjunction of Venus with Saturn a malefic (1) both are in a benefic sign and benefic varga, (2) Saturn is the lord of the 4th, (3) Saturn is yogakaraka. The same conclusion can be arrived at by an examination of the Matrubhava as per the system of Jaimini. According to Jaimini, the Matrukaraka is the fourth in rank as per the number of degrees advanced by planets in their respective signs. Mercury comes first having attained 28° 27′. Next comes Saturn who has got 28° 21′. Next Venus 28° 9′. The next is Jupiter who has got 19° 12′. The 4th from Arudha Lagna has also to be taken into account and that is Taurus. Jupiter is a benefic and the fourth from Arudha Lagna is also a benefic sign. Taurus is a fixed sign and all movable signs and the planets located there aspect Taurus except the next sign of Aries. Therefore, Mercury a benefic aspects Moon (in Taurus) as also Mars a malefic (for Cancer, a movable sign). Jupiter the Matrukaraka is aspected by benefics as well as malefics. So the mother will have a fairly long life. As we are in Matrubhava, it should form part of the forecast as to when her demise should take place. It is likely to take place about the end of Rahu Dasa. Rahu is in the sign of Jupiter who is aspected by the lord of the 4th house, Saturn. As he is by nature a malefic, he is likely to appropriate to himself this function. The function generally falls on the lord of the 4th house, or Matrukaraka, or planets associated with them as also the planet that occupies or aspects the Matrubhava. Jupiter is lord of the Navamsa containing the lord of the 4th house. He is in the 2nd from the Moon, the Matrukaraka. Thus Jupiter's qualifications are clear and it is only to be judged whether Jupiter or

Rahu will handle the business. Rahu is more likely. In the Amsa Rahu is associated with the lord of the 4th and is in the 2nd from Matrukaraka, the Moon. Of all the planets connected with the 4th house, Mars is the greatest malefic who is also debilitated. As he is really in the 9th house, he does not aspect the 4th house directly but aspects the 4th house by distance (opposition) and also by his special and powerful 8th house aspect. The sub-period of Mars in the major period of Rahu takes us to 21-11-1969. There are also rules for determining the time of demise by transits to bring it within definable limits. Subtract the figures of the Moon from those of the Sun. Find what sign the remainder represents. When Saturn or Jupiter pass through that sign and Navamsa or through the triangular positions corresponding thereto, the demise of the mother may take place. The Sun's figure is 10-13-38. Subtracting Moon's figure which is 1-1-41 we get the remainder 9-11-57. This represents the sign Capricorn. In March 1969 Jupiter would transit the triangular sign of Virgo. Saturn would be in his debilitation sign of Aries which being the twelfth sign from the Moon heralds the beginning of sadesati.

Education.—This has to be judged from the entire horoscope and the 4th house is only indicative of the academical distinction that is likely to be attained by the native. The 2nd house also indicates Vidya or learning and the 3rd house denotes cleverness or mental characteristics. The 5th house indicates the real learning or wisdom of the native. Here Mercury is also the Atma-karaka. The lord of the 4th house is with a benefic and in Vargottamamsa, as well as aspected by Jupiter. Mars, the lord of the 4th from the Moon in the Navamsa is with Mercury and therefore also aspected by Jupiter. The aspect of Mars to the 4th house in the Rasi and the combination with Mercury in the Navamsa will impart energy to the native in the prosecution of studies. Thus whether the native is clever or not, he will get high academical qualifications to a certainty because of the prominence and strength of the 4th house. Saturn, if he is concerned with the 4th house or afflicts it, is liable to cause obstruction in the persuit of studies but he is the lord of the 4th in Rasi and yogakaraka in Navamsa. The only way in which he interferes is by aspecting Vidyakaraka in the Navamsa, but as Jupiter also aspects and Jupiter is the dispositor of Saturn both in Rasi and Navamsa, his aspect will not cause much mischief. Still there may be occasionally slight breaks or disappointments. The association of the lord of Lagna Venus a benefic and Saturn lord of 4th in Rasi and Navamsa is noteworthy and deserves to be made special mention of.

Branch of Education.—The Bhavamadhya of the 4th house falls in Capricorn, an earthy sign. It is occupied by Mercury the Vidyakaraka. The Moon an important planet where mind is concerned is in Taurus—also an earthy sign. Both the Moon and Mercury are in earthy Navamsas. The predominence of earthy signs in connection with Vidyakaraka makes the native either scientifically or commercially inclined in the pursit of studies and utility will loom prominent in his view. Such persons though rarely quick or brilliant are more often painstaking, persevering and plodding. Three are three planets in common signs and two planets in the fixed and two planets in movable signs. This gives versatility to the native though he may not care to be thorough in any pursuit. All these features should be taken into consideration. The fact of Mars aspecting the 4th house powerfully from a

watery sign should not be ignored. This combination
sugsests study of engineering, specially hydroelectric or
technology in oil, or such allied persuits. Mars lord of
the 4th from the Moon in Navamsa aspects the 4th, is
with Mercury and is aspected by Saturn. This indicates
also ordinary engineering of heavy machinery where fire
and electricity too are employed, but this is secondary and
should not be the main object of the native.

Luxuries and Conveyances.—If the lord of the 4th
house is strong and is aspected by or conjoined with a
benefic, the person will have at his command vehicular
facilities. Saturn, the lord of the 4th, is not only aspected
by benefic Jupiter but is also conjoined with Venus,
another benefic. Mercury another benefic is in the 4th.
Another peculiar combination which confers vehicular
facilities is present. If the lord of the 11th house reckoned
from the lord of the 9th be in the Navamsa of the Atma-
karaka planet, then also the native will be able to
command vehicles. Here the lord of the 9th is Mercury
and he is in Capricorn, the eleventh from which falls in
Scorpio. The lord Mars is in Virgo which is also the
Karakamsa. Hence this yoga is present. It can even be
said that as all the principal benefics are connected with
the 4th house, the native should command a multitude of
vehicles. The 4th contains Mercury and the 4th bhava
therefrom contains waxing Moon. The lord of the 4th is
with Venus and is aspected by Jupiter. The eleventh
house is concerned in the matter of ownership of vehicles
and it has been already seen that lord of the 11th Sun is
aspecting his own sign. It is noteworthy that the 11th
from Lagna is also the fourth from the Moon—a unique
feature in this respect. Venus is not only a benefic but
also a karaka for vehicles, etc., and his conjunction with

the lord of the 4th and aspect from Jupiter has a special significance in this respect. The Amsa indications are also favourable in this matter.

Paternal Property.—We have found that the 4th house is particularly strong. There are no contrary indications for this. So the native can expect to inherit substantial paternal property as well.

Children.—In Chart No. 125 the 5th house falls in a fruitful sign namely Pisces, but its lord is in the 6th a dusthana. To compensate for this as it were, the lord of the 5th house who is also the Putrakaraka receives the aspect of two natural benefics, Mercury and Venus. Mercury is, however, lord of 8 and 11 and hence evil for the horoscope. The 5th house though untenanted by any

Chart No. 125

Jupiter	Rahu	Mars	Merc. Venus	Rahu	
		Moon			Sun
RASI				AMSA	
			Mars Sat.		Jupit.
Lagna Saturn Ketu	Mercury Venus	Sun	Lagna Moon	Ketu	

Balance of Mercury Dasa at birth : Years 14–11–0.

planet, benefic or malefic, receives the aspect of a malefic namely the Sun, who, by being the owner of a kendra has become a complete benefic. Thus a sort of balance between the good and evil influences has been effected. From the Moon the lord of the 5th Mars is in the 12th house. In the 5th itself, a firstrate malefic Saturn is found who is the lord of the 7th and the 8th from the Moon. While the ownership of the 7th is very good the ownership of the 8th is very bad. There is no aspect from any planet either to the 5th from Moon or to the lord of the 5th from Moon or even the 5th from Jupiter, the karaka. Therefore as from Moon, which cannot be ignored in this case as he is strong, the testimony is not so good for children. In the Amsa, from Lagna and the Moon, Rahu occupies the 5th and its lord though exalted is in the 2nd with Saturn. One redeeming feature, however, is that Jupiter aspects the 5th and the Moon occupies the 5th from Jupiter. But Mars also aspects the 5th. Here again the balanced position seen in Rasi is maintained. From all this, one can conclude that while the native will have a number of children, the family will not be large.

The same conclusion follows even as per Jaimini. For this the Upapada has to be found first as that will be more or less the centre point from which this matter has to be judged. Upapada is found by counting as many signs from the lord of the 12th house as the 12th lord is from the 12th. Here the 12th lord occupies the 12th and so the 12th or Libra is the Upapada. We have to examine the 5th from the Upapada and as this falls in an odd sign and the 5th from lord of Upapada falls in a fruitful sign, there will be a number of issues. The lord of the 5th from Upapada is aspected by both Jupiter and the Moon as well as the 5th from Upapada. But Rahu aspects Upapada also, and Mars and Sun aspect the 5th from the lord of the 5th from Upapada. These are contrary indications and so the same balance between good and evil forces are seen.

Number of issues.—The cusp of the 5th house falls in 350° 47'. Hence 6 complete Navamsas have been passed. The lord of the 5th house is also Putrakaraka and he has completed 5 Navamsas in that sign. The Sun aspects the 5th and he has also completed 6 Navamsas. Saturn is in the 5th from the Moon and he has also completed 6 Navamsas. The Sun is also the lord of the 5th from Putrakaraka. Therefore 6 is the number almost uniformly indicated as being the number of issues and the distribution will be four males and two females. Loss of one or two issues is likely as lord of 5 is in 6 and lord of 5 from Moon is in 12. A malefic aspects the 5th from Lagna and a malefic is in the 5th from the Moon.

Speculation, etc.—The discussion of the strength of the 5th house for children holds good for this aspect of the matter also. Speculation will result in gains as well as losses and much of the losses can be eliminated by choosing the right times only and confining to those occasions for speculative activities. The aspect of Venus on Jupiter, while in one sense good as from a benefic, is not so as he is also lord of 12, the house indicating losses. The aspects also indicate losses arising through divided interests, through carrying on two occupations at the same time or through too frequent change of occupations.

The 5th house being a watery sign aspected by the lord of the 10th, the native will have journeys by water several times not only for the sake of business or occupation but for pleasure also.

The 6th house represents enemies, sickness, debts, etc. It also governs inferiors, servants of all kinds and service. In so far as we subordinate ourselves to anything, whether it is an ideal or a person, we identify our activities with this house. There are no planets in the 6th

house either from Lagna or from the Moon in the Rasi
(Chart No. 126). But in the Navamsa, Rahu is in
the 6th from Lagna and the Sun, Ketu and Jupiter
are in the 6th from Moon. The lord of the 6th in
Rasi is in debility in the 8th house. The native is
likely to have a wound or scar in the face or head
as the lord of the 6th is in the 8th bhava conjoined with
the Moon and Rahu. The bearing of this bhava on health
and sickness should be discussed under Lagna bhava. Three
classes of planets have influence in connection with any
bhava—the lord of the bhava, planets in the bhava and

Chart No 126

	Saturn	Rahu Moon	Merc.		
RASI		Venus	Moon	AMSA	Sun Jupit. Ketu
		Sun Mars	Rahu		Sat. Lagna
	Ketu	Lagna Merc. Jupit.	Venus	Mars	

Balance of Sun Dasa at birth : Year 1–9–18.

planets aspecting it. Here there are no planets in the 6th.
The lord of the 6th is weak with malefics. But of the
planets aspecting this bhava, the Sun and Mars, the Sun
is stronger, being in his own sign and in Simhasanamsa.
Mars is also in Gopuramsa. So, the promise of evil concerning this bhava denoted by the weak lord of the bhava
will not only be belied but also be replaced by benefic

effects.   So life will be fairly healthy upto very old age
and measures taken for ills and for conserving health and
vitality will bear fruit to a great extent.

Enemies, debts, etc.—Troubles from these sources will
be reduced to a minimum and will not occur for any
major concern.   Saturn's Dasa period of 19 years (1963–
1982) will   not be entirely trouble-free in this respect.
Even with regard to Saturn, there are redeeming factors.
The lord of the 6th in the 8th constitutes a yoga.   His
debilitation is more than relieved by his being retrograde.

OM TAT SAT

An Index of Technical Terms

Adhipati	—Lord.
Adhipatya	—Lordship.
Apoklima	—3, 6, 9 and 12 Houses.
Arudha	—The sign which is distant from the lord as the lord is from house concerned.
Bala	—Strength.
Balarishta	—Death in childhood.
Bhachakra	—Zodiac.
Bhava	—House or signification.
Bhrathrukaraka	—Indicator of brothers—Mars
Budha	—Mercury.
Budha Dasa	—Mercury's period.
Bhukti	—Sub or Minor period.
Chandra	—The Moon.
Chandra Dasa	—The Moon's period.
Chandra Mangala Yoga	—Angular disposition between the Moon and Mars.
Chara Rasis	—Movable signs, e.g., Aries, Cancer, etc.
Dasa	—Period.
Dhanakaraka	—Indicator of wealth—Jupiter.
Dhanus	—Sagittarius.
Divya Drishti	—Intuitive perception.
Drekkana	—1/3 division of a sign.
Dusthana	—An evil place.

Dwiswabhava Rasis	—Common signs, *e.g.*, Gemini.
Dwirdwadasa	—2nd and 12th from each other.
Ghati	—Equivalent to 24 minutes of English Time.
Graha	—Planet.
Guru	—Jupiter.
Guru Dasa	—Jupiter's period.
Guru Bhukti	—Jupiter's sub-period.
Hora	—½ division of a sign.
Jaimini	—A Maharishi of India. Author of works on Philosophy and Astrology.
Jathaka	—Horoscopy.
Kanya	—Virgo.
Karaka	—Indicator.
Kataka	—Cancer.
Kendra	—4th, 7th and 10th Houses.
Kendradhipati	- Quadrangular lord.
Ketu	—Cauda or Dragon's Tail.
Kuja	—Mars.
Kuja Dasa	—Period of Mars.
Kuja Bhukti	—Sub-period of Mars.
Kumbha	—Aquarius.
Lagna	—Rising sign or Ascendant.
Lagnadhipati	—Ascendant lord.
Makara	—Capricorn.
Mandagraha	—Superior or slow-moving planet.
Maraka	—Death or death-inflicting planet.
Matrukaraka	—Indicator or Mother—Moon.
Meena	—Pisces.
Mesha	—Aries.
Mithuna	—Gemini.

Mitra	—Friend
Mitravarga	—The Varga or the place of a friendly planet.
Nararasis	—Human signs.
Navamsa	—1/9th division of a sign.
Naisargika	—Natural.
Nirayana	—Fixed zodiac.
Ochchabala	—Exaltation strength.
Ochchabhaga	—Exaltation degree of planets.
Panapara	—2nd, 5th, 8th and 11th Houses.
Papakarthari Yoga	—Being hemmed inbetween two malefics.
Putrakaraka	—Indicator of children—Jupiter
Rahu	—Caput or Dragon's Head.
Rajayoga	—A good combination for political success.
Rasi	—Sign of zodiac.
Ravi	—The Sun.
Ravi Dasa	—The Sun's period.
Ravi Bhukti	—The Sun's sub-period.
Saham	—A sensitive point.
Sani	—Saturn.
Sani Dasa	—Saturn's period.
Sani Bhukti	—Saturn's sub-period.
Satru	—Enemy.
Satru Bhava	—Sixth house.
Sayana	—Movable zodiac
Shadbalas	—Six sources of planetary and house strengths.
Shashtashtaka	—6th and 8th from each other.
Shastiamsa	—1/60th division of a sign.
Simha	—Leo.
Sthirarasis	—Fixed signs, *e.g.*, Taurus.

Sushka	—Dry or Earthy.
Sukra	—Venus.
Sukra Dasa	—Venus period.
Sukra Bhukti	—Venus sub-period.
Swavarga	—Own sub-division.
Thula	— Libra.
Thrimsamsa	—1/30th division of a sign.
Thrikona	—1st, 5th and 9th signs.
Udu Dasa	—A system of Directions.
Upapada	—The sign as apart from the 12th lord as the latter is from the 12th.
Vahanakaraka	—Indicator of conveyances —Venus.
Vahanasthana	—Fourth House.
Varga	—Manner of division, e.g., Rasis, Hora, etc.
Vargottama	—A special distinction.
Varsha	—Year.
Varsha Dasa	—Period relating to the year.
Varshaphala	—Annual results.
Vidyakaraka	—Indicator of education —Jupiter.
Vidyasthana	— Fourth House.
Vighati	—Equivalent to 24 seconds of English Time.
Vimshottari	—A System of Dasa or Directions.
Vrischika	—Scorpio.
Vrishabha	—Taurus.
Yoga	—Special combination.
Yogakaraka	—Planet causing yoga.

—o—